D1596688

In the
meantime

In the meantime

Elizabeth Smart

DENEAU

112664

Published by
Deneau Publishers
411 Queen Street
Ottawa, Canada K1R 5A6
© Elizabeth Smart

First printing 1984

Cover design by Anita Bergmann & Jan Soetermans

Canadian Cataloguing in Publication Data
Smart, Elizabeth
In the meantime
Includes poems.
ISBN 0-88879-105-4
I. Title.
PS8537.M37I58 1984   C811'.54   C84-090133-X
PR9199.3.S63I58 1984

Printed and bound in Canada
by John Deyell Company

iv

CONTENTS

Foreword   1
I.   Scenes One Never Forgets   7
II.   Eleven Poems   25
III.   Dig a Grave and Let Us Bury Our Mother   43
IV.   Poems from 1940   95
V.   New Poems   109
VI.   In the Meantime: Diary of a Blockage   131

ACKNOWLEDGEMENTS

Some of these poems have appeared in the following magazines: in England: *Tribune*, *Tuba*, *New Departures*, *Only Poetry*, *The Literary Review*, *PN Review*, *Big Bang*; in Eire: *Cyphers*; in Canada: *Toronto Life*.

Eleven Poems was originally published in 1982 by Owen Kirton (Publishing) Bracknell.

Grateful thanks to the Canada Council for a Senior Arts Grant that made possible a re-experience of Canada.

FOREWORD

In 1982, Deneau reissued in hardcover, Elizabeth Smart's celebrated *By Grand Central Station I Sat Down and Wept*. The history of this novel's publication (2000 copies were first published in England in 1945; it was reissued in paperback in 1966 and published in North America in 1977) attest to its continuing growth in popularity and acclaim and to its reputation as a literary classic, a poem-novel unique in style and sensibility. In 1977, following thirty-two years of silence, Smart published a slim volume of poetry, *A Bonus*, and a poetic prose work, *The Assumption of Rogues and Rascals*. Both works were critically hailed and further established the reputation of Elizabeth Smart.

With the publication of *In the Meantime*, Deneau makes available for the first time, a collection of Smart's writings, a collection that brings together poetry and prose, much of which is unpublished, in out-of-print magazines, or inaccessible. For this reason it is an important collection and one that sheds light on Smart's creative forces, on the on-going process of her writing, and on the evolution of one of Canada's most distinctive stylists.

The selections in *In the Meantime* span a period of forty years. They include poems and a novella written before the publication of *By Grand Central Station I Sat Down and Wept*, selections of recent poetry and prose, and the republication of *Eleven Poems* published in England in 1982 and hitherto unavailable in Canada.

1

The early poems (written in 1940) and the novella, "Dig a Grave and Let Us Bury Our Mother" (1939), are reminiscent of the style and the concerns of *By Grand Central Station I Sat Down and Wept*. The poems deal with the power and the passion of love and betrayal and are set against a background of impending war. Like the novel, they rely heavily on image, metaphor, and conceit and recall the metaphysical poems of Donne, Herbert, and Vaughan. "Dig a Grave and Let Us Bury Our Mother" explores the complex connections between mother and daughter and the relationship between two young women. It also shows the burgeoning of the style and sensibility that will distinguish *By Grand Central Station I Sat Down and Wept* as a literary classic.

The selections of later poetry and the prose pieces "Scenes One Never Forgets" and "In the Meantime" move from the earlier preoccupation with love, passion, and betrayal, to the concerns of a writer coming to terms with her life and with the continuing struggle to write. There is a consequential shift in the later work to a more elliptical and aphoristic style and philosophical and compassionate viewpoint.

An interconnection exists in Smart's writing characterized by the exploration of the self in relation to an external world. In "Dig a Grave and Let Us Bury Our Mother," the narrator says: "I am the only thing I know. And even that I only see through a glass darkly from time to time, as a great way off." Yet it is not a mythification of the self that sets this exploration apart, but a relentlessly honest search that transcends the impulse to document or to confess by extraordinary perceptions and the power and beauty of the language. *In the Meantime* is an evocative collection and provides an intriguing glimpse into the life and mind of a fascinating writer.

Alice Van Wart

I

Scenes One Never Forgets

I am 63, the happiest person in the world.

But I still cry out at night, heard throughout the house, through several walls, still wrestling with infantile anguishes and anxieties.

"Mother! Mother! Mother!"

It makes a rude intrusion into the pleasant sleep of the dinner guests; it jolts the nerves of the deeply-sleeping drinkers: an involuntary inhospitality.

"Mother! Mother! Mother!"

Desolate. Eery. Desperate.

Long ago, forty years or more, a beautiful young woman was tender towards me, took me into her mind, her life, her bed; and I thought I had laid my mother's ghost.

But no. Faceless memory breaks through the decades' disciplines, all the carefully collected consolations are scattered, shattered by the eruption of the first fatal separation.

Re-entering the past is a dangerous adventure. I fear the giant waves, the icebergs cruelly clashing in the lifeless landscape.

I fear you will fear them too.

But you ask what happened.

Yes. Well, we had a wonderful childhood.

But are not all childhoods wonderful, are not all unique?

An old woman shows you her trophies, urgently, passionately, salvaged from a life she has mislaid along the way; as if these faded snapshots were magic mementoes that would bring back the thrill that living once had, that will make you see and feel what she, that unique she, once saw and felt.

Look! Look! they seem to say: I *did* exist. I was here. I had moments of triumph. I had visions, amazed glimpses of the possibilities of being alive. For a while, even, I was the most beautiful, the cleverest; when I was born, I almost remember, I was the most important person in the whole world, to my mother.

But, friend, onlooker, didn't you throw away those old snapshots you found in the derelict house?

Of course you did. They lacked the art to stay your hand. Like a million million others!

So.

One life is all lives.

What will you save out of your dead days?

Does it matter if the wedding dress was white or gold or pink? Or if the lover's eyes were blue or black or brown? Or if hunger and rags and earnest respect for pennies eked out your penury, or luxury suffocated and constrained you?

What remains is only the electric pain lighting all; the kiss softening the parched face.

Passions flash, illuminate.

Combing through the debris, telling each day as it was, or seemed to be, each week, each year, each decade, do we find anything? Is there a light on the matter we missed? Shall *I* find anything that might interest *you*, sitting there so still in your own great irrelevant heap of days?

If we aren't careful, we get a mountain of microfilm, indigestible even to computers: layer upon layer of masking fact, identical twins with identical IQs shooting from outer space, or glancing off council house or castle wall in an indiscriminate multiplicity and confusion of the I-am-I.

One true word: let it stand for what we don't remember.

But still, you say, what happened?

People are greedy for details. A set scene establishes order.

And the old men are writing their memoirs: generals, cabinet ministers, rarely-defeated boxers, colonial administrators are setting the record straight, the sacred record. "I was there. My being there was not unimportant. I saw it all. *I. This* is how it was."

Yes, it was magnificent. But it was not war.

And you were looking in the wrong place, in the wrong way, for the wrong enemy.

The ordering of the world, that chaotic household, is a very little thing. Three strong-armed scrubbers could get it into shape, could clean up the messy births and deaths and semen-strewn sheets, and put the flowers in rows.

Then what, then what, vociferous politician?

Your squalid clamour obscures the soft sweet issue, and cancels out your life as well. For you don't know what you do. Or *why*. If you only knew how your hidden greed shows through! No hiding for secret meanness: even the mediocre have X-ray eyes, and all is revealed, as the years go by. It shows in the face; it shows in the deeds. Not this year, maybe, or next. But hourly people with brand-new prejudices come along, and the old ones are dropped, the ones that made your props; and little by little the simple sum is done. This spells your doom, hyprocrite, liar, cheat. You could avoid humiliation, but you think you'll get away with it, not realizing how the rules all change.

Look at the poor Victorians: their snotty little secrets all laid bare, below their grand and gorgeous goings-on. Their loud splendours lasted out the day, and we all cheered.

Well, if the *day* is all you want . . .

Their great-great grandchildren peck about among their papers, calmly, curiously, holding up the grubby findings to delighted light. Euclid explains how two clues hold the third. Sleight-of-hand can only last for life, often less.

I peck about among the flotsam of my own past, looking for clues to the origins of ancient storms, storms that still rumble ominously. Mysterious memory seems eccentric, arbitrary, but early scenes recur and keep recurring. I pick them up for your inspection.

I found myself sitting in a sandy pine-wood. I got there by walking along a splintery board walk. Everybody had run away. A hot seductive breath of wild strawberries rose around, half consoling, half calming, but fear and apprehensions clung. I could see sand-dunes with tufts of spiky dangerous grasses, but they hid so much: the fear that nothing was behind them, around them; the fear that something *was*. Everything was the enemy but this soft silent sun-soaked moment. My bare feet prickled, alien with splinters.

Before this I remember . . .

I trudged upstairs, shooed by maid? nurse? mother?

Unwanted.

The baby slept.

I trudged on up, steps steep as Everest, revengeful, helpless, scouring the world for a small clutch to hold on to.

Where did I go? Rejected, up into the dark, with difficult steps on two-year-old legs: an ineradicable memory of a journey with no arrival.

Weren't there any warm cosy moments? I must have known there could be, for I screamed and screamed and screamed at the top of the stairs (some lower stairs) for my mother to leave her friends and gossip and cakes and tea and come.

But she never came. Or if she did for punishment, banishment into the huge deserted nursery, and the laborious folding and mating of those thick white woolen stockings and placing them two by two in virtuous rows, furiously concentrating, desperately muttering: *Now* are you sorry? *Now* do you see how unjustly you abandoned me on that lonely landing?

Where were my sisters? Where were the servants?

What a mist that childhood is.

Yet it was that plump rosy baby, whose sacred sleep shooed me off, who found that her childhood had chewed away her life.

I said, truly, we had a wonderful childhood.

I found consolation. I found the woods, the wildflowers, the lakes, the birds, animals wild and tame.

At school, labled "clever," I had to hide it all, make light of it, to try to capture popularity, a necessary camouflage, not to stand odd and conspicuous, a figure of painful fun. Here the two-faced business begins, only half successful. But the other girls gave me marks for trying, and sometimes making them laugh, and modestly keeping hidden all I knew, and my mad delight in learning. I played at being mad; they understood that: a clowning camouflage.

This was quite a dexterous feat.

Now, I ask myself, twisting and turning for my own survival, could I have taken full maternal responsibility for a little bewildered sister?

I could have been warmer, more sympathetic, more open, more explanatory: a comrade, a teacher at least of what I knew. But I was secretive, cunning, bent on survival, devious.

And later, decades later, developing these warmer qualities, which I reproach myself for not having had *then*, I regret their development, for undermining my purpose, mumbling "par delicatesse j'ai perdu ma vie." (While the ones who think I ride roughshod over all sneer and murmur, O yeah? O yeah?)

Still, a melting heart makes the purpose infirm.

Give me the dagger!

If you don't know life-saving, the clutching arms drown you both.

Murderous impulses start early. The baby cuckoo is born with murder in his heart. His flimsy featherless shoulders, just out of the egg, heave and heave, and hoik and hoik, until they've spilled all foster siblings over the edge of the nest to death. Born, looked round, found murder necessary.

A scene recurs. I am about four years old. They have gone down to the beach without me. They have taken my little sister, not me. I am left behind. Their gay voices have got fainter and fainter.

"I want to go! I want to go!"

But Granny holds me back.

"You're to stay here with me."

"I want to go! I want to go!"

"Be a good girl. Come and help me pack."

"I won't! I won't! Let me go! Let me go! You're a brute! You're a mean pig! Let me alone!"

My grandmother's bleak face towers above me. Her thin arms with the loose flabby flesh bind me like steel. She is invulnerable. I can kick her and hurt her, but she is inflexible. Her mouth is drawn tight. Her glasses have grown misty, watery. She locks the door of the room. I kick it until my foot hurts. There are black marks over the white paint.

She starts packing a trunk. I hate her. Her aggrieved face is hard like stone. Her disapproval is set. She doesn't understand me. She has no sympathy. She has no right to touch me. How dare she! I hate her. I hate her.

"I hate you, Granny!"

"You're a rude ungrateful girl."

"You're mean. You're cruel. I hate you. I hope you fall in the trunk and get all bloody!"

13

I saw her gasp of shock. I am shocked too. I dared! God might hear me and punish me. She might fall down dead. She might be struck dead and bloody.

Her mournful voice intones: "I won't be here to trouble you much longer."

I feared that tone. I feared her tears. Her unfair weapon was tears. The embarrassment was terrifying. Death the unspeakable hovered.

"No, Granny, no."

"You'll all be glad when I'm gone. You'll all be glad to get rid of me."

"No, Granny, we won't."

"I know you all think I'm a nuisance."

"No! No! No! I like you, Granny."

"Hmph! Pretty funny way of showing it!"

I was silent. I couldn't apologize. But it would be terrible if Granny died. I could have killed her. It would be all my fault.

"Will you apologize?"

"No."

"You ought to be ashamed of yourself. If you don't apologize I shall tell your mother everything you said. Will you say you are sorry?"

"I'm sorry I was rude. But you were mean not to let me go to the beach."

The release when they came back! The relief to feel when you kicked and screamed that your enemy was strong and could stand it! Granny's watery glasses, her suffering put-upon look embarrassed too painfully, made me feel too mean, made the doubt that killed the joy of battle.

I hid in the rhubarb patch. I told it everything. I sat there until I forgot. Until now.

"Raking up the past." Raking to make a seedbed?

How smooth the tilth of the good gardener.

"Digging up the past." That's archeology, more respectable. Rougher work: you can't rake before you dig. You can't *find* before you dig, except bits that time leaves protruding, one great paw, half-exposed in the shifting sands.

Rejected, I ached to please, somehow, by hook or crook. I hoped to attain praise, if not warm encircling arms; approval, a light, a look in the eye, at me, at ME, to give me a place in the universe, to confirm my existence, as I stood there shivering with doubt and fear, and nowhere to go.

I remember little ruses: shitting in my pants long after the baby stage, to be babied again to bed, cleaned up; pretending to be asleep to avoid rebuke, to be handled, looked after, at last, again. It seemed so long since paradise was lost.

I see that look so often on ousted babies, who thought they had things proudly under their thumb, and the world doing their bidding, until they found themselves sitting alone, and the world rushed off to crow and croon over the vile usurper.

They are amazed, flabbergasted. How could that deep love melt away so soon? We were all-in-all to each other; Mother, Mother, how can you suddenly cast me away with scorn?

You are old, whiny, wet, clingy, uncouth, nothing to be proud of, no asset for an adult.

But we seemed locked in endless bliss!

That was yesterday. Get a move on up those stairs.

When you are very small, and afraid, and you wake in the night, escaping from a bad dream, the loud ticking of the nursery clock reassures, lays a wholesome hand on your wildly beating heart. It is china and has painted birds of blue with flowery tails. It stands on the bureau. It is polarity. Time ticks away childhood, but in the night it whispers intimately. Five minutes, in childhood, having no precedent, stretch out like years: time for the familiars in the flying dust to speak, and the child's heart to break.

No one loves me. That warmth went by me, ignoring, to my rosy sister. That nest, *my* nest. I am hiding behind the boxes in the dusty attic. I am hollowed out by my unheard screams. My flaming throat is hoarse. I shall be lost. I shall stay here for days, crying and starving. They will find me dead and be sorry. They will remember how they once loved me and say *how* can we have been so mean! They will beat themselves on the attic floor, fling themselves on my dead body, howling and screaming the way I am howling and screaming. I shall fly in my ghost-state to the window and watch them crying. I shall cry for pity to watch their terrible remorse.

They? Not they, really. *Her*. My mother. Those loving arms. That warm state, lifted above fear. That bringer of sunny dreams. They don't come. They don't hear. But there are no more screams to express my bottomless woe. I am exhausted. My face feels strange and puffed.

I shall be good. To make them love me more, and be ashamed. To make their misery greater when they find me dead. I shall go downstairs and tidy my bureau drawers. Every one. I shall put the white stockings in rows. It will be hard work. But I shall do it.

The long work. The aching. The never-ending rows of white wool stockings. It is hard. It is agony to work like this. But I shall exhaust myself. Perhaps I shall die with hard work. Then I shall be a heroine, dying doing good. She will know how she loved me once she has lost me. She will take me in her arms and kiss me, crying and wailing. Oh it will be terrible, her tears and moans. But nothing will do any good. I shall be dead. And she will remember me always. Everybody will know. It will spread about the world. Like the little boy with his finger in the dyke. But he did not die. I shall really die.

Work numbs me. I am aching with tiredness. Perhaps I shall lie down. The work is only half-finished. But I'd better lie down. Sleep pulls and pulls. I am dropping into the kind clouds of sleep. Dry tears tickle my cheeks.

Brushing like a great soft wind over me, my mother comes with her soothing gentle face.

"My little Betty," said in the strange darkness suddenly descended. O pity pity for those horrors of misery in the dusty attic, rushing like a dyke let loose to that breast that was balm.

"O Mummy! Mummy!"

"Mummy's here, don't be frightened. Mummy will protect you."

I had been left out, left out. They had all rushed strongly by and I didn't know where they went. I was lost and alone. Nobody cared. A pitch black night came down.

"My darling, hush! Mummy won't leave you. Go to sleep, my baby."

The clouds of protection, the relaxing love. Let this continue. Let this surrounding never end. A lullaby, a lullaby. She loves me. I am the one she loves, my special Mummy, she loves me specially. She sings and I drift. Into her love and sleep.

Older, I made awkward advances to my father, stroking his chin, commenting on his bristle. This he found obtrusive, insensitive, tactless, embarrassing, and tried to teach me better. I saw, knew, recoiled. Another bid for love hit the dust.

Still, there developed a long intellectual concept of such things, a tender love that never touched.

Is this why my lovers have never been counted in dozens?

Every object it rolls against moulds the stone.

But I am not explaining; history is only observing which way the stone rolled.

The confusion of those first seven years! The incomprehensible games of my older sister and her friends; the heartless laughter at my bewilderment; the running-off in Run-Sheep-Run and leaving me; the daze of doing and never knowing why or what or where. Just observing, observing: water, mud, dust, snow, moon, trees, dandelions, heat, cold, food.

Pain could attach itself even to food: forced to eat up, gagging on gristle, revolted by parsnips, outraged by the slimy blandness of milk toast. But there was also joy and jollity. When it was lemon jelly my sister and I rolled off our chairs, hysterical with laughter saying "Lemon Jelly! Kiss my belly!" And there were secretive chicken timbales, where a de-

18

lectable creamy filling broke out of a crispy batter-cup. And there were candies brought in amazing boxes and bottles by stranger uncles; and olives, and the pride of liking such grown-up foods; and pretty sugar-sticks in jars.

Still, on the whole, childhood seems all about love and separation, love and longing, love and rejection; a stupor of love unsatisfied; the hopelessness of making oneself understood, helplessly bombarded by incomprehensible pain, the little comforts and jollities few and far between.

Stupefied, dead, and buried.

But the facts, the same facts, (if there are such things as facts, which I doubt), were seen differently by others. It was different for my sisters, either for better or for worse. My mother's friends saw it far from the way any of us saw it (*"You girls had a wonderful childhood"*).

But I didn't see it, or anything, then. I see it now. I was confused, dazed. I went into a dull dream from two to seven, punctuated by screams of rebellion, pathetic efforts at drawing attention to my merits. Dimly I perceived adult doubts about me, suspicions that I might be mentally defective.

There were the triumphs of kindergarten, and pleasure in my mother's pride. (I could see that it came as a surprise, too). I marched at the head of the column, with my sturdy little chair, upside-down on my head, *leading* the others! I made neat well-praised mats of woven paper in mauve, yellow, green, blue, red, and had a deep relationship with each emphatic shade. I knew with heady skill which little battered desk to sit at, how to march in a circle to the music, even singing the correct words to the song.

Two years of this and I almost had it made, but wham bam next year I found myself in a huge class without a clue, and strange hates directed towards me from inexplicable teachers, and more rumours about my half-wittedness.

I trailed to school after my big sister, not even knowing the way, and she far ahead, taunting, complaining, scolding, making mock.

And I remember the strange kerfuffle about the man who sat on the fence and exposed himself; and the man in the vacant lot who took me boldly by the arm; and I remember the adults' consultations and conspiracies about these events: tut-tuts, excited shock. *I* felt nothing, I never had, did; I felt cosmic sympathy for these old tramps, I reached for a kinship. I realized that the adults were twittering up the wrong tree, tactfully questioning, worried about the effects on "sensitive little Betty."

No, no. One registered, that was all. The seas that rocked one, wracked one, were in other principalities. I felt for the poor tramps, pursued by harpies for a harmless foible.

I also noticed, with dismay, how the big girls egged the adults on, taking mean advantage for a shoddy little bit of drama.

It takes years for the pattern to appear.

And we *did* have a wonderful childhood, thrilling to the frothing surf on the bland sand of Brackley Beach, Prince Edward Island, or making leaf houses in the woods by the lake at Kingsmere; going for walks with Daddy, begging to be thrown into flat round juniper bushes, just prickly enough for ecstacy; finding enchanted flowers in Flower Ben on the first cold picnics; taking the adventurous first trip up to the cottage, wondering if we could get there, because of the congealed snow on the road, packed down in old drifts, and patches of ice. Then we roared with joy and spring. How we must have driven our patient father frantic, bellowing out of tune, loud, excited, *A Hundred Blue Bottles*, from one hundred relentlessly down to one.

Scenes one never forgets: an older sister's dress torn off, her half-formed secret breasts exposed, her face slapped, while hysterical sexual monumental fears flashed off an enraged, panicking mother.
Such scenes do not occur in the logical sequence autobiography strives so often to put them in. Why strive? Memory recurs in flashing scenes: A small body sobbing on a bed of maple leaves.

We had a wonderful childhood.
But I am 63. I still scream.
So the past is still with me, battling to get out, like a well-embedded thorn that can only be expressed when the poison gathers to a head.
Or the future is still lurking round, battering to get in, an inflexible, teutonically determined bee that won't buzz off.
Something is still unresolved.
Though we did have a wonderful childhood.
And my life now is as perfect as a life can be.

II

Eleven Poems

THE MUSE: HIS & HERS

His pampered Muse
Knew no veto.
Hers lived
In a female ghetto.

When his Muse cried
He replied
Loud and clear
Yes! Yes! I'm waiting here.

Her Muse screamed
But children louder.
Then which strength
Made her prouder?

Neither. Either
Pushed and shoved
With the strength of the loved
And the unloved,

Clashed, rebuked:
All was wrong.
(Can you put opposites
Into a song?)

Kettles boiling!
Cobwebs coiling!
Doorbells ringing!
Needs haranguing!

Her Muse called
In her crowded ear.
She heard but had
Her dirty house to clear.

Guilt drove him *on*.
Guilt held her *down*.
(She hadn't a wife
To lean upon.)

"The dichotomy
Was killing me,"
She said, "till old age
Came to assuage."

"Now! Muse, Now!
You can have your way!
(Now . . . what was it
I wanted to say?)"

Used, abused,
And not amused
The mind's gone blank —
Is it life you have to thank?

Stevie, the Emilys,
Mrs Woolf
By-passed the womb
And kept the Self.

But she said, "Try
And see if it's true
(And without cheating)
My Muse can do."

Can women do?
Can women make?
When the womb rests
Animus awake?

Pale, it must be,
Starved and thin,
Like hibernating bear,
Too weak to begin

To roar with authority
Poems in the spring
So late in the autumn
Of their suffering.

Those gaps! It's decades
Of lying low;
Earth-quaked, deep-frozen
Mind askew.

Is it too late
At sixty-eight?
O fragile flesh
Reanimate!

Eschew, true woman,
Any late profligacy
Squandered on the loving of people
And other irrelevency,

Useful in the dark
Inarticulacy,
But drop it like poison now
If you want poetry.

Let the doorbell ring
Let the fire men
Put out the fire
Or light it up again.

Sheepish and shamefaced
At nine a.m.
Till the Muse commands
Her ritual hymn,

See lucky man
Get off his knee,
And hear now his roar
Of authority!

This test-case woman
Could also be
Just in time for
A small cacophany,

A meaningful scream
Between folded womb and grave,
A brief respite
From the enclave.

A WARNING

This old woman
Waddles towards love,
Becomes human,
But the Muse does not approve.

This going flesh
Is loved and is forgiven
By the generous,
But houses a demon,

Hullo, my dear, sit down,
I'll soothe your pain;
I've known what you've known,
But won't again,

Though passion is not gone,
Merely contracted
Into a last-ditch weapon,
A word not dead,

A mine unexploded,
And not safe
To have near the playground
Of innocent life.

Keep clear of this frail
Old harmless person:
Fifty year's fuel
Of aimed frustration

Could shatter the calm
And scald the soul
And love fall like napalm
Over the school.

URGENCY AND ENERGY

Urgency
Brings energy.

And energy
Makes urgency.

From urgency a dying poet speaks.
From energy an adolescent wrecks.

One with a purpose
Heaves old bones,
Risks collapse
For what he knows.

The other, filled
With unholy rage
For holy strength
He cannot gauge,

Hurtles towards hurt,
Destroys his day:
By blind mistake
Iconoclast.

Missions, omissions,
Dangerous needs!
Pray shaping spirit
Supervise their deeds.

BIRD AND ADOLESCENT

How well birds
manage their bodies.
Look how they shake off
the rain,
cheerfully surveying
the prospect
for interesting
things to eat.

Where are they huddled
when they're not
hopping about;
when it's all silent
and the air is empty
of their
flighty forays?

A while ago
they were so
busy and thick
you almost collided
with them
walking across
the lawn.

And now, nothing.
Each in his retreat
waits
in rain-enclosed
silence.

Suffering?
It seems not.
They sit,
in expected acceptance,
wide-eyed
for the next
development.

How could you explain
this to an
adolescent,
throwing himself in despair
into a deck chair?
Hurling his turmoil into the calm air —
if it's clouds for him it's clouds for all
So there!

But after time passes,
perhaps,
and his mind clears,
he sees the birds there,
and round unclouded eyes
stare out
bright rebuke.

PUB POEM 1: THE MERRYMAKERS

When you've done well
There's nothing to tell.
"Help! Help!" cry the prisoners.
"Don't bore!" say the revellers,
"A pint, a bird, a mighty cockstand!
Defeat is not on our mind.
We replenish our stores,
We've nothing to buy from bores.

"Bones like 'Life' we've gnawed all day:
It's time for play.
The best jokes are thrown off along the way."
See them retreat, the prisoners,
Into an eating silence,
Grey, pent up in the corner.
Catatonic! Impotent!

Mercy, merrymakers!
Not every day is a great making day.

PUB POEM 2: TREACHEROUS SURFACES

I said: "All surfaces are treacherous
All depths are well.
Hold my hand while I tell."

But he was lecherous
And broke the spell.

I see: all art is unnatural.

PUB POEM 3: EXCHANGE AND MART

Exchange and Mart:
You can't have this
But I'll give you that.
Hullo! Have a pint!
Not praise but a kiss.
You'll have to make do
With what is:
You help me, I'll help you.
A financial swizz!
Sometimes a block of gold
For pins!

But *someone* benefits:
The market spins!

WHAT IS ART? SAID DOUBTING TIM

It's *not* leaving your mark,
Your scratch on the bark,
No, not at all
'Mozart was here' on the ruined wall.
It soars over the park
Leaving legions of young soldiers
Where they fall.

Dido cried, like a million others.
But it isn't her tears
That sear the years,
Or pity for girls with married lovers
That light up the crying I
With the flash that's poetry:
It's the passion one word has for another.

It's shape, art, it's order, Tim,
For the amorphous pain;
And it's a hymn,
And it's something that tears you limb from limb,
Sometimes even a dithyramb;
A leap from gravity,
That feels, in the chaos of space, like sanity.

The maker makes
Something that seems to explain
Fears, delirious sunsets, pain.
What does the rainbow say?
Nothing. But a calming balm comes
From Form — a missile that lasts
At least until tomorrow
Or the next day.

THE SMILE

What does it mean
The smile on the face
Of the embryo?
From nine months' nesting
A comfortable afterglow?
Or a smile of triumph
For getting where a million million others
Failed, but
Wanted to go?

It's not like the smile
On the face of the newly dead.
Though people say peace
Achieved at last,
Face relaxed,
Frowns ironed out.
No triumph there
When we get to where
We have to go
Whether we wanted to or no.

The smile on the face
Of the nearly or
Newly born
Is beatitude, is bliss
Far beyond ignorance,
Or absolute comfort
In a safe cocoon.
What can it mean
That nobody ever enters the world
With a frown?

A MUSIC NOTE

Sometimes Handel
is loud, triumphant, insistent.
I want to say Shut up!
Can anything really be *that*
successful and sure?
It must be a lie
and a noisy one, too.

Then he introduces
a note of soft seduction,
and I am abashed,
and ashamed,
and blush
to the music
of the spheres.

END OF A SUNFLOWER

A pheasant found a sunflower,
And perched on the arch,
And munched,
A little every day at an early hour.

What a way to go —
Obscene remains ragged on the tall stalk,
Startling the tactful dying all around,
The soothing autumn sinking-away-in-a-glow —

A murdered man on show!

III

"Dig a Grave and Let Us Bury Our Mother"

(from William Blake's "Tiriel")

I am escaping. I am putting miles of sea, continents of desert and impassable mountains between us. But her fatal electricity can not be avoided. It penetrates every insulation. Now there are revengeful dreams where she catches me and drills her fierce will into my escaping life. I cower stock-still, trembling with fright. If I hit back the pain is excruciating. To see the softness so wounded! Worse than the symbolic jellyfish destroyed so long ago by my angry foot. (My father said, "Why kill it?" And I cringed and crumbled with shame, and realized the unredeemable murder I had done.)

My mother is always a thing too big and soft to attack. I batter with my fists, but only rose-coloured yielding softness meets me. The softness. The pathetic tenderness of the softness.

I am escaping those storms that curdle the stomach. I lie in the sun wooing sleep, lapping the generous day. But her huge face appears in the sky, insane and askew. It melts and disintegrates into a child just learning to walk. I wake shivering.

There I was, going steerage to Mexico, hoping for help from geography. I welcomed the stark conditions. I took the vomiting body of humanity to my bosom. I loved their greed over the last tutti-frutti cake, their fears, their imaginary ills. I felt lulled in the rough arms of Poseidan himself.

I said, smiling, when I had to lie on the canvas cot, and they vomited on all sides, so that it splashed into my face and the stench was everywhere: O I am in the thick of it; I love love love this humanity, my humanity, my people.

It was in 1939. The ship was full of refugees coming from Europe to a neutral Mexico. They were full of hope, the relief of escape. It synchronized with my own hopes, relief, escape. I smiled all over and thought: Not one man am I expanded to, but all men and all women. Come what may, if they should do this or that forbidden thing, I can only yield. I am all open and have no resistance to offer, only love.

Smiling, smiling, rocking on the stern sea in my stern bed. Through the foreign languages the friendliness, the backnotes better than through words understood. But most of all the intoxication was the adventure.

Then, as I slept, suddenly a voice permeated through saying "Betty! Betty!" There was a knocking at the dark porthole, and one after another the fourteen women in my sleeping place were waking in their bunks and speaking. "Betty! Betty!" was tossed from mouth to mouth. I sat up shaken from my warm dream. A dark-eyed face at the porthole discovered me. A cable had arrived. The long arm had reached me. I was to be taken immediately to a first class cabin. No refusals. Come along, come along. Reluctantly, regretfully, I followed up and up through the cold air from my healing depths to my sentence of luxury.

44

O the unprivacy. Discovered in my lair. Always that tyrannical love reaches out. Soft words shrivel me like quicklime. She will not allow me to be cold, hungry. She will insist that I take her own coat, her own food. INSIST. Can I refuse? Can I make a harsher discord with ungraciousness? Not yet, not yet. I am escaping, not escaped.

The insulating comforts: how men hug them as if they enhanced life. When I was in my loving-bed below, I thought: what things do most people fear to lose? What things are most clutched by most? I thought: after virginity is lost, the world can be your lover; rape loses its horror. Before, the unthinkable unknown startles, alarms, sets the adrenalin flowing for wild flight. The refugees had been through all. Especially hunger. They eyed the cakes. An old lady, plump and battered, fingered each one as if it were the clue to survival. Others in their relief flirted, were consoled by success. Others did things to make them appear a man in the eyes of men. How they loved the advancing of the *mal-de-mer*. Heralded gloomily and gloatingly its approach. Groaned and retched with what full relish. They savoured gratefully the return of the omnipotent petty, ordinary everyday events.

She was like this. But she was not like this. She could have a fellow-feeling for suffering humanity. She would give food and warm clothes and sympathy when people died. She would respond to the forlorn sagas of brave cleaning women. But she believed in the great class barriers. One had a duty to stay where God had been pleased to put one. Naturally she had been put at the top. ("If the best's not for me who's it for?") Any infringement, any sign of impertinences, of liberties taken and the claws came out. This feeling of divine right was not hers alone, of course. A long stable majestic century accentuated it, and in Canada where nothing ever happens it must have been even easier to believe in it. A strange vanity — that one is born superior, cannot but be superior, whatever one does, however one lives.

She would have killed my happiness in my chaotic steerage life with one glance from her eyes like a firing squadron. "Ugh!" she shivered, and its echo reached me a thousand difficult miles away.

Down below, we had dinner at two wooden tables in a sort of cement cell, crowded on wooden benches. I felt part of a great tradition. I felt I was taking my part with everybody else, taking things as they came, anonymous, alive to all eventualities.

Now, can I sustain my great adventure in this too familiar comfortable isolation? Cherished, guarded, padded, my work will be doubled. I must break through these lulling clouds, and translate when I get there. But to have refused this first-class ticket would have meant another kind of cloud. All through the tossing voyage I would have been seething, angrily defending myself to myself, wrangling with my conscience. How could I have kept open, stopped trembling? And I was a marked person after the purser sought me out. How could I have explained to fourteen grateful refugees my inexplicable desire to travel steerage?

However, the escape continues. It is, after all, the beautiful before. My cosy pink pajamas lap me round, silk inside and downy wool outside. A large amiable scrubbed stewardess gives me breakfast in bed. The sky changes into a dozen different blues. The sun is happy and all-assuring.

O the beautiful beginning. I could lie here tasting it, cherished by these tender pajamas, cosy accessories, tasting the day, which is entirely mine, of which I can make what I will.

For not one evil binding thing is in me now. My insides fly like air. I can do anything. I am full of love like thistledown. If a burly sour person should get in my way I should laugh, as if he were an angry cub with his eyes just open; I should relish his ridiculousness. Any approaching event can only be richer and richer.

I watch with interest the drama of my friend Eva, clutching her violin, leaving her love behind. Her ropey face, parched and battered, looks as if it had been exposed to hopelessness too long. It has no inside resistance. Yet she, alone, is leaving all, is making the brave break. Her lost girl lover waited below as the boat got ready to sail, grew chillier and chillier, standing alone and blue on the dock among the screeching people. How Eva suffered; I felt her pain, I saw her drama. But I was cocooned by my delirious escaping.

Eva's palliative and lugubrious scales and arpeggios break through my sleep, and the grey-white porthole's discouraging eye.

"There is always work," she said.

And so, through my sleep, the yards and yards of unnecessary gymnastics, like soporifics or magic repetitions to soothe her pain. A long, even, melancholy necklace from her faithful violin.

"You do me good," she said. "How do you manage always to be so happy?"

I put flowers in my hair and trail across the dance floor. But I am in the enemy I fight, like Jonah in the belly of the whale. There is no escape yet from that umbilical cord that winds round me like a hangman's noose.

These days all sky and sea are wild with innuendo and submerged life. The greens, blues, whites, half-greys, large embryonic clouds float with the unformed bigness of potentiality. The whitecaps of foam, the gulls' flight, the strong warm wet air, full of spring messages, go through everything, through every pore, the brain, the sex, the mouth, the hair. The soft wind ravishes, exhilarates, possesses. O to leap, to leave the endless becoming, to be sea, be sky, be wind. But whose will, though voracious for self-denial, can hasten the metamorphosis?

The sea's rhythm is enveloping, surrounding, adoring, expanding, at the sky's melting meeting. The origin, the back-box, from which all love emerges, flows back. Why cling to a match-stick polarity?

This morning there was sun again, making things merry. I heard laughing voices, an upsurge of hope, rising spirits. But suddenly an unknown man's voice cried menacingly: "This time you've got to apologize!" and my blood shied, everything froze. I remembered that tone from those catastrophic quarrels my mother engendered, that had to run their course, freeze a week of terror-struck days.

Be sea, be sky, be wind. But I am not sea or sky or wind. I am this upright person thrust into the world too soon, still searching for the womb I lost. I suck my lover's lip frantically, as if it were a breast and I starved for milk.

I say "lover," but he has no features, no name to shatter my peace. When I think of him I think of the great expanse of warmth where his shoulder is. I sank into that. I merged, melted, dissolved. He came into me, but it was me falling away into him. I, burrowing deeper and deeper, until I could be surrounded on all sides in that unborn state. He was becoming my womb. Is that a lover? I am flying from him too, no menace, but no use either. Lying by his side, an echo of my mother's voice descended like a tropical tempest, devastating my newfound home. My bare body felt her whip. The ground grew spikes. I found myself stilly conceived in my synthetic womb. I repudiated it.

Why can I not explain or describe her? Could I reconstruct her yearning girlhood, with Emerson and Matthew Arnold in leather binding under her arm? My father took her in a canoe one day when they were twenty-one. They paddled softly up the canal under the weeping willows. She took off her great white hat and laid it across her knees, trailing her hand in the water. Her dress was white too, with a high neckline up to the throat, her long swan-like throat. She thought: He is looking at me, but I shall not let him know I notice.

"We have known each other for a long time, Miss Parr, would you allow me to call you by your first name?"

Behind the tree, while he laid out the tea, she rubbed her nose surreptitiously with a little chamois leather, surrounded by real lace. My love is very pure! Two souls communing! In the company of the great departed ones! "A noble and a true conceit of godlike amity." How sweet to discourse with one who understands.

She tucks her chamois leather into her bag. Her dreaming eyes strain after Emerson. "Be good sweet maid and let who will be clever." Did she make herself cheap to allow him the use of her first name? A little prouder, a little haughtier, in case. Her contrary skirts are reflected in the shadowed water.

"Will you take tea now, Miss Parr?"

"I am not hungry now, thank you."

Arnold! Emerson! Your ambiguous signals, your severe mistakes, bore these years for me.

She could spread sun. She could be a radiator of light. She smelt sweet. Her serenity could be like the wings of sleep, when it was in possession of her. Sometimes she sang lullabies and was a pillow against nightmares, toning and tuning all things that went on around her. Why couldn't this state last forever?

Her storms descended quicker and direr than typhoons, more deadly because her sun had opened your locked doors. You lay vulnerable, naked in the calm air, and the unexpected shock charred you, made you recoil, turned your insides to stone.

Mexico, a new country. For my eyes new distractions. Worlds of other beauty. My eyes have grown as large as dishes, but they overflow still. My eyes are large and strenuous. My voice is silent, left behind like the backward moss. Speak, fool! Tell the marvellous your eyes have seen, but that flows so fast off its slippery surface, round, fickle, rolling. If only eyes could hug and store, but like the stomach they can only hold so much. They devour, swell, drop away again.

The listening evening dissolves the sluggishness. Arise slug! Over the strange desert, over the mountains, roams the revelation. Make me a prophet, then, to father the quick gold meaning. Darker darker the mystery closing down until the blind mind looks within, is joggled will-lessly and floats in a pool of contemplation, takes shelter from the night. *Is afraid of revelation.*

These blind protective mists are terrible. They confiscate every sense. They annul all antennae.

Should I make a list, a resolution of will power? Would a list rouse a slug?

Tack-a-tack! Tack-a-tack! A sound in the dusk. Voices, skulking dogs, geraniums breathing, the smell of wood smoke.

Expand, expand, into the homogeneous mystery.

I can't.

What is poetry? Do not enquire. The secret dies by prying. How does the heart beat? I fainted when I saw it on the screen, opening and closing like a flower, though I had said I wanted to see it. That was my life out there, frail, fluttering. No wonder we insulate ourselves from wonders. Poetry is like this, it is life moving, terrible, vivid. Look the other way when you write, or you might faint.

The dark cactus shapes emanate in the gentle night, the bananas in paper bags wait like petitioners.

What was it you wanted to ask me, rejected lover? I turned away from the answer. You too avoided. The answer is too frightening. It is escaping on all sides in terror. You might as well grab evanescence here as there. Are your hands webs? In the libraries of dust, maybe. But it would be pain indeed to have no fingers in the night for love. Here! Here! the panting part cries, and only a webbed wing floats over the flesh dying for a touch.

My mother — this mystery that pursues me — I only know I tremble and do violence in my dreams. Or she turns to a little child and I give her pleasure for her own good. Or I fight her great soft body.

Insulator, rejected lover, now I find the world cold. But I suppose I had a reason for thinking it would do me good to cross this desert alone.

These violent dreams! This confusion! When will the water be clear? I cry for a lover. Or I cry for a hermit's rod. Or I clothe myself in buffer mists.

Sleeping alone, the night rears in and possesses me with fierce fearful dreams. I remembered and weakened towards the sleeping companion whose presence made a nest of rose clouds that remade the unravelled day.

Yesterday I entered my face in a rose. Be a rose, woman! I said. And fell to plotting ways.

And do you know the rose never washes? Dew and rain wait upon her so dutifully. She breathes luxuriantly. Woman, did you hear? Perfume to make the senses rock!

Under the feathery-leaved tree, with the mountains on all sides, the pale dried maize-fields rustling all around, the cactus swords in rows between clouds, the valley in a haze, I begin to feel the idiosyncratic earth of this unknown land. I begin to sing its tune. The small yellow butterfly or the escaping lizard have the same rhythm. I am at last again a continuation of the ground I walk on. The dust, even, is part of it. My feet have a union of harmony, and the rocks I jump from hug, then render up in passing, their essence.

I am staying with friends, a man and two women; it is a *mariage à trois*. All is warm and stimulating. They are Europeans, concerned with writing, painting, ideas. They bolster my freedom. I revel in this airy cut-off kingdom of Ruth, Peter, Maud.

Ruth's beautiful palaces I could walk into, wide-eyed and innocent, and betray no one. I feel I could bring her my distrustful soul, unmasked, tender, and unafraid.

But Peter's palaces would be harder to enter without a crowd of betrayals. Why? In his I'd start with fear, feel shameful, bound, companioned by ghosts, and premature regret. I feel I'd find no wells springing, heart to heart, no soul with her Pandora box. I sense a game, guilt, cringing, a forgive-me-this. But is this caginess on my part a betrayal of myself?

I gnaw these matters.

In the bath I thought: So much of life is *waiting*. But later, on the sofa, the solitary moment flowered and serene feelings flooded. Riches poured. I thought: This is the full vibration! A sea of silence surrounded it. It could be savoured. It was a conscious moment. Every article in the room blossomed, promised seed. There seemed to be no reason for this moment of such happiness. But I knew: LIFE BEGINS HERE.

Music is the harmoniser, the suggester, the absolver, resolver, fecundator, bringer of tears, and whipper-up of the blood. I abandoned it. But for that lost liquid world I now receive a recompense: gradually the adjacent earth speaks, there is a slow slow growth, there is a sudden light breath on the neck as the chairs and tables break into flower, and the walls' dreams show their motion in the clearer listening air.

The trembling on the threshold. Were all thresholds trembling always? Two outward eyes watch. I hear a death-chorus of the world's superstitions. A mask-face. The legend of Narcissus. Outward tangible gestures never come out of my secretive psyche. My heart is a bouncing gazelle. Nothing is more contrary. It listens; it waits, hidden in its nearby thicket. It trembles too.

"Christians!" Peter scoffed.
"Ronsard!" he scoffed.
"Oroszco!" he scoffed.
"Rabelais, Corneille, and Racine!" he scoffed.
"The Bible!" he scoffed.
Love, I am knocking at the door: for God's sake let me in! I mean, don't let my eyes get narrow, don't let me pick and pick in secret onto the nursery wall. Let me not scoff just to scoff, to think I can explain timeless miseries. Let my chase have a beast in view.
A bad seed sprouted. It grew and grew. Fanatically. I began to despise and hate Peter for despising

and hating. For what he calls "discipline," for his lack of wonder and joy, his belittling of almost everything, his doughy baby face, his untouchedness. I chewed on these things secretly and began to look madly for any escape. Then, in the mirror, I saw my bumpy face and small aggrieved eyes. I remembered: the menstrual tides are due. Wait. Do nothing. Think nothing, until nature is let loose. Then perspective will be truer. You'll know what's what.

But the bad seed grew, and produced a day without joy at all, even though I smelled a rose, and went to the old part of the town, and read *Moby Dick*, and ate a sugar plum.

Maud met us in the candy shop, and we had coffee together with Peter. She is sweet, and angelically patient, but she cringes and agrees and is afraid of the seas that cleanse and strengthen.

"I don't believe in tolerance at all!" cried Peter. "It's just that lax attitude that produced the atrocities of the Christian bourgeousie. In that fuzzy-headed atmosphere idiots can flourish."

He knocked down everything so that even the flowers in his own garden wouldn't flower.

Christianity was the reason for everything ill. Rabelais did harm. The English never produced anything. The Americans will never produce anything. Look at these people's faces! Ugliness and stupidity everywhere you look!

But Peter is a painter, or wants to be. His mind pursues so indefatigably his irritation with the people he meets that he has not the eyes or the repose or the love to see a yellow tree or a red-tiered cloud, or a beggar's blue shirt.

"These people! How they persecute one and destroy one's peace!"

He wants to shut out more and more of the vulgarity of the world from his island dictatorship, where he rules infallible.

But Ruth carries her beautiful hanging gardens with her wherever she goes; soothes him, smiles, watches when the light changes. Her fingers caress life's pulse. Life flies by him and he grumbles because he feels a draught.

All this makes me guilty. I hate myself for the small-eyed look. I regret my necessary reservations. But to me the stupidity is not to be alive. Peter flirts with surrealism. But surrealism, they say, in their pamphlets, is the marvellous, anything that is marvellous is beautiful. Has he marvelled once these last two weeks? Has he laughed like Rowlandson at another's quirk rather than been annoyed? Has he loved the flavour rather than despised the measurements of the persons he was forced to be with? And was he ever forced anyhow?

I thought, at first, he was a delicate instrument, pale with what he received, whom thought poured through. But no. He is bound in swaddling bands of pedantic dogma, and thinks the truth can be laid out flat on a map.

It would be heaven to achieve harmony with every person and place forced on one. And harmony would be the St. Peter's key to get you into this heaven. If you carried it who could threaten you with excommunication?

His face is doughy, I told you. Yes. It makes me want to sere it with the lava of pain, seas of tears, whips of rebuff, hunger, desolation. I want to weather it, seam it. The little dictator in his satin-lined tower, curling his lip over spawning life below. A telescope to see the stars (that meticulous instrument of science) is, after all, only an elongated pair of blinkers, such as a horse wears, so he can not see too much and be afraid.

Why do I speak so much of Peter, then? Why do I step down and begin to carp? Do I fail now? Am I forced?

Again, he is that electric hate, that contagious possessiveness I fly. He begins the day by knotting my stomach at breakfast. His voice pierces the environment with a damning note for all who do not agree. He begins the day by dictating and damning.

Ruth tries to put forward a view.

"Childish!" he says. "Not thinking clearly! Not seeing before your nose!"

I dare not venture to get that scathing rebuff. She only ventures timidly. He says: It is thus and thus; all who do not agree are fools! I dare not eat my toast because it goes down in lumps and turns to stone in my stomach.

Is it this peevish boy who wields the weather over my soul? Or my mother's long shadow, her stinging underlying echoes echoing still? Is it like the malaria germ, or dysentery, irrevocably in my blood?

Ruth weeps. But it is her private drama. Maud sees nothing amiss; she knits, adds up the accounts. I am free. I am here by my own will. But it is on my face that the nervous bumps break out. It is I who wake in the night in a cold sweat.

Peter makes tentative gestures of contrition, concern, humility: flabby overtures when only a whirlwind would do.

I walk up a mountainous pine-lined road, erupting luminous clouds. There's a tang in the evening. There's an ashes-of-roses valley. It is a hoard to gloat over at the day's end. But there is something else. A richer note; a more disturbing note.

Two eyes of red reflecting heater. Ruth talking. Richness, all possibilities of a human being unfolding, stranger, more unexpected, more exhilarating than a fern. Her tenderness — what she makes of love, bringing back the mythical fragrant groves, the sunset gestures to be made into the legends that stir the heart.

Why have I not spoken more of this land that was to distract my haunted eyes? Ruth says because it does not make love to you. It has no blandishments. It does not pull you by the hand. Can any but a corpse kiss dust? The evocative smells seduce one to become one with their source. But if there are no smells what thread then? What O Arachne to lead to the lair where you will be captive with love and bound to the soil, the essence of a place?

"Abstract," Ruth says. "Nothing breathes. You cannot mingle with the sprouting life as you walk along the roads, because it does not sprout."

I lie on Ruth's unmade bed. The two heaters reflect. Ruth, half-weeping, trails about her room in her long velvet negligee. She paces. (O echo of pacing mother doing gymnastics of parental pain.) I watch her obliquely.

"When I look in the mirror I wonder who it is," she says. "It's like being drunk. You look and look and say who's that? and move from side to side to see if it moves from side to side too and it does so you

58

know it must be you. I have got so old since I came here. There is no love in the air. In all these months I have only seen two couples walking in the moonlight holding hands or putting their arms around each other. I could as soon make love to those shoes or the table or the bed as to the people I have met here. Cold, absolutely cold. And the flowers have no smell. The climate kills the sweet smells but intensifies the bad. Even sterilized Americans stink here; but the roses in the garden are odourless."

But her real loveless landscape is Peter's dying heart. It is his growing thorniness that brings her this desert.

"Couldn't we escape to the sea?"

"Peter needs me."

"He has Maud."

"That's not enough. He needs someone to consult and advise him about what he is doing and thinking, to help him with his work."

"It might be good for him to be left alone. He could have some of that discipline he's so fond of."

"He doesn't like discipline. That's why he talks so much about it." (He was scornful when I said I wanted to help a man I knew. "It's sentimental of any woman to think she can help any man. It's adolescent," he said. But he has two women like a pair of crutches, and even then life harasses him too rudely. And his pearl watery and unborn).

"I don't want to be an egoist," Ruth said. "I hate people who are always irritated and dissatisfied with their surroundings. Usually the slightest thing gives me great joy. I can be happy over nothing. But all those months of travelling and adjustment — it confused me. You adjust your eyes to something very far away and suddenly something very near is put in front of you.

On and on she went in a monotone. Her beautiful face that usually radiates in a miraculous way was drooped and colourless; her voice sad and tired, but with the urgency of its message. Her Buddha hands wandering. Wilted flowers, pleading, feeling the sadness, afraid to ask life themselves least they lack elegance, but ravenous for love, frantic with life slipping away.

One evening Peter was ruder, more destructive, more negative than usual, slapping me down, killing the possibilities of the moment, and I rushed out baying at the moon, calling apologies to my discarded lover, wanting, wanting, wanting what? The moon looked withered in a great circle of tired greenish light with two desultory stars unwinking, unresponding. No life whispered in the breathless dust. I called upon Rima, Junta, Undine, legendary sorority sisters, and thought of their fates: one fell into a sea of flames crying her lover's name in vain; one fell from Monte Cristallo brokenhearted when they destroyed the crystal mountain; one melted into the anonymous murmuring stream tears and all.

I am caged here, caged, caged. They fear — what? They people my blackness with their own ghouls. I am in that blackness (that dazzling light) and I fear *them*. How can people worshipping their blind ego strike down brutally the delicate upward surge, the tentative heavenward flowering of another human being. Peter struck that down! He forbade me to flower! His cruel rule must be absolute! Where was a shoulder of refuge for me? Who could protect me from brutality and assure me I have a right to be? I lurked in the garden, but the moon's pale effort sent no alchemy. I remembered that other night when I repudiated my lover and sat shivering by the dark water-lapped wharf, and later ran across the fields stumbling, crying, disconsolate, desperate, for then it was the consoling shoulder that had melted away and there was nowhere to run.

It is a mythological mountain I run towards when I run. But here, how can I reach it, fenced, compromised, wearing my warring dissembling high heels? Saying, after all, this soft strange painful thing, man, is what I must know. Take outward clothing like his, listen, be hurt, but say nothing, wait. In time, with much love, all will be revealed.

Ruth came down the garden path in her coat and said,

"Oh darling, don't cry."

Peter behind her, smirking apologies, peering white-faced out of the shadows.

But his words were to me like being stroked with a crutch.

Ruth soothed. Her sympathy was dry and gentle. She would be the world's lover-mother. She was all tenderness. But I felt her struggle.

Peter brought me a book. He was concerned, contrite. He did not understand what I cried for. Not anger. An accumulated sorrow pertinent to the whole world. I cried for his sorrows as well as my own. I had no focal point. I cried long after he ceased to be the cause. By mistake he turned the tap and the waters flooded through.

Less and less I am able to speak, to tell, to know what is in my mind. It is fear of breaking down the multiple images. I don't look for any confidante, have no craving even for the impersonal listening of such a one as a psychoanalyst. I only want the covering, the merging. There is a fear too of not being able to *receive* if there is any too-definite thing in the mind, or obsessive feelings causing static to reception. My machine, sensitive and open, receives and receives and never reacts.

But mustn't things be sharp and vivid, mustn't I *care* one way or another? I see this side, I see that side, but with which side do I side?

But fair fights are only with mutual weapons. If there weren't a deficit to be made up, a want, I might be able to speak.

I must see clearly, dare to speak, rouse myself to examine, not flop into the moment. I must know, put it all, gathered and whole and true, into place. Dissemble, but *know why*, and watch.

But supposing I feel nothing, nothing at all, lying a livid registering instrument, otherwise paralyzed? Would a lashing at last bring livelier results? Would simulation generate the seeds of a true feeling? I fear the cold frightened repulsive image of unresponsiveness!

Does my unresponsiveness spring from fear, bound to me with the whips and spikes of my mother's words? Or my fear of fearing? My fear of not greeting graciously the throbbing supplicant minute?

I do not know why, but that desert with the Devil's Pit, where we three walked, comes back and back and is the setting for many of my imaginary scenes, and sees my unborn passions act.

Ruth leans over me as into a pool, her hair falling, her eyes eternally smiling, but like jewels smiling, their smile cut out eternal and unchangeable, her mouth too, stretched and smiling, the eternal smile, a woman taking pleasure in a dream. And her whole smiling face, with its frame of dark falling hair, is like a reflection. Her glance smiles on, only the water makes it waver and tremble. The smiling gaze penetrates me and is unceasing.

I am uneasy with the threshold, the portico of sensual love. I do not know it, or how to deal with it. I never could return an eye's gaze. I know the lonely image-building, I know the escaping in order to be followed, I understand hands held but heads that look in opposite directions, undeclared communion, and I have entered jubilantly into the abandon of the night, the losing of self, the melting, passionate heaving of becoming one with another.

But the savouring, the lingering, the articulation of Sappho with her girls in the flowery grottoes. "To me, Sappho, you are like the lotus unfolding." Here my eyes become wild animals who have never seen human beings, they dare not watch love approaching. Their terror makes them mad for escape, or freezes them stockstill.

I am a blunderer here, heavy-handed, a new world tourist in the Buddhist temple. I hate my inexperienced tread, my brusque inadequacy. Can I not melt too in tenderness, or is my home always to be the wilderness? Can I not become an image gazing at an image, and not the distant analytical one, saying what next? Will her earring fall when our two mouths come unglued?

Tentative, tentative, the tendrils creeping from the frozen plant onto this unknown ground. Creeping, too, in the light of day, consciously, without the impetus of passion, without a forgetful cloak, or the covering of darkness. It is a dance, but the watching eyes are pained.

I dreamt a long dream of unscrupulous satyrs with watermelon mouths, and of escaping, and of indoor swimming pools, tiled and vaulted, and then of my mother and a flock of sexual babies. My mother had liked the preliminaries, not knowing or suspecting where they led, but when she came back from contact with the satyrs she was terrified, terrified. A satyr had tried to put his hand under her dress, she said. "Look!" she said, and she lifted her skirt and showed me how she had sewn her underskirt together into a kind of below-the-knee bloomers, with great untidy stitches in sailor's strong thread. She was defiant, but I touched her face and it was petrified. All over she was hard lumps. I was filled with compassion for her terror, arising from ignorance, so I sat her down, sprawled in a chair, and told her to relax. "Now your toes," I said, and she relaxed her toes, and I went all the way up, being careful, I remember, not to mention any indelicate part. Gradually she thawed out, and I went away to a cafeteria to get something to eat.

I sat up in the dark, listening. Suddenly the distant train's steel shrieked like a trapped woman, and afterwards the masculine pursuing whistle sounded, low and predatory.

Ancient pyramids, religion springing from dust, a desert's breath; at last a beautiful backdrop, pink earth, pink houses, red and green trees with intimate bunches of translucent drooping fruit, drooping leaves; dismembered antiquities offered in smiling brown children's palms; the Pyramid of the Sun, neat and geometrical, but squatting on the ground, satisfying the comfortable longings, a re-affirmation of solidity; a deep well and six faces peering in like a pariah; Popocatapetl's fierce gleam when everything else grows grey; pools of water and a strangled sea-like mist which descended until I strained to join it, slipping back to water, slipping and swimming and escaping; or the fearful purple mountains, batting back eyeballs, whose horizon have a greenish tinge ("It were a vain endeavour Though I should gaze forever"? No, I leapt too in fiery tiers).

But above all this, enwrapping all this, the tenseness, the electric touch that disintegrates joy. With all these wonders, why does Peter blind himself with protestation, hate, cramping irritation, half on his seat, the gold day riotous outside.

"Oh these fools! These idiots! Ask over there! Go a little further and ask!"

Lumps of swelling vexation bump and batter me, and I observe Ruth's fatigue, her face turned to a sad-coloured stone, her mouth set. Opened as I am to her I cannot escape the weather she exudes. My stomach turned hard and hurt me, and when I saw my own mouth in the little glass it was sullenly drooped.

A gay pink and blue house flashed by; patches of yellow worn thin, trees of paddle-cactus in voluptuous frozen rhythms. I leapt up, but then I leapt back guiltily to my droop. The desert, the faded yellow desert, the grass stiff with sterility, the dust swirling into the seeking nose. The pink-tipped porous volcanic stones. The scorched crumbling desert's face.

Peter seeking possessions. Peter dictating. Peter condemning. Peter fearing. Ruth cynical, sad, resigned, tired, lifeless. Maud the faithful trotting servant, her face like a skull, her shoulders huddled into herself, a continual rebuke.

I melted outside the window, into the multitudinous vivid clouds, or the pools, or the trees, or the hills, to harmonize, to loop my life on, to be able to say Love this one willy-nilly, pity the weakness, not condemn; people only behave like that because they are ill or unhappy or incapable of understanding. A not too scrutinous eye can merge with that ditch pool's water. They speak of Undine, but can they *know*, if that shimmer has no power at all?

Lying on Ruth's bed, the eye of the heater encouraging, Ruth talked and wept.

"It isn't anything to do with religion," she said. "I just *feel* it. I can't help it. I feel personally responsible whenever I see suffering. My sympathy hurts me. I felt like this even as a child. Always. I used to ask: Why is suffering? Why? Somehow I felt it was my fault. I could *do* something about it."

"I only know what I feel. I don't understand abstract things, cold things. If I feel, I know; and I don't know unless I feel. André Breton was all wrong when he spoke of the cries of pain and joy of a woman in childbirth. Joy! Once outside my window a woman was run over by a taxi, the taxi cut her in two, across her head and across her legs. I heard her screaming for a long time before they came and took her away. And another time when I was in the hospital I heard a woman in childbirth. I assure you, the cries of these two women were exactly alike, as frightful, as terrified. The woman in the maternity room was not crying for joy. Why does such suffering have to be? Why? All the time I listened I felt such terrible shame. I was responsible. Peter scoffs at Christianity, at all religions. And even as a child, when they tried to tell me about God and His goodness, I thought, how can there be a god when such things happen?"

"You saw how mad Peter got at breakfast when I said I thought the bloody Quetzacoatl sacrifices were just as bad as the bloody Spanish persecutions practised here. The pity! I can't help feeling pity. It's not religion. I feel it, that's all. And I feel the responsibility."

"Of course, the thing that draws you to a man is to feel you are needed. Peter is dictatorial and intolerant, never thinking about me. But on the other hand he is one of the most intelligent, really intelligent men I have ever known, and I have known a lot of men. He has such a lucid view of the world. But he should paint all day and write all night. He is not made for a normal pleasant life with other people. He's too tense, bursting with his new ideas. When he was young his body didn't develop very fast, so his brain grew and grew, became the chief thing. He was locked up with his scholarly books. He never learned how to live. But he makes me feel he needs me, that I can help him. When I was sick, coming here, and they were afraid I was going mad, Peter was in despair. He came to me crying, saying, "Don't die! Don't die! You must you *must* get well!" and for a couple of weeks afterwards he was much quieter and thoughtful to me, doing sweet things, making tender gestures."

"And, also, he's one of the most generous men I've ever known. If anybody, even someone he doesn't like, comes to him asking for money, and he has it, he gives it. And not only money, he has helped all sorts of people in all sorts of ways you'd never imagine. He really has a warm and generous heart. And some of the things he has written are remarkably moving."

She talked on, sometimes weeping, sometimes moving about her room, telling about her earlier lovers, about Peter's first mistress, a woman old enough to be his mother, whom he still wrote to and wanted to keep in his life.

Then Maud opened the door and came in to measure some curtains she was making. Ruth jumped up, wiping the tears from her eyes, and went out on the balcony. Maud smiled placidly and went about her business.

We lay out on the balcony sunbathing. Ruth rubbed oil all over her body; I rubbed it on her back for her and she rubbed it on mine. We told each other we were beautiful and worshipped the sun, looking at each other through our tangled hair.

The morning got so gay that I thought all would be well, but at lunch Peter's first word, harsh and autocratic, shot out of him like lava. I didn't hear what he said but I noticed the morbid hush. Then I saw a round tear slowly going down Ruth's cheek. Peter saw it too and it infuriated him. My tortillas stuck in my throat, grew corpse-like on the plate. No one spoke. Even Maud was hushed apprehensively. In a few minutes he got up and went across to Ruth's chair and put his arm around her.

"It's nothing, dear," she said, "Don't trouble. It'll be over in a minute."

So he went back to his chair. But her tears slowly followed one another. Everyone's eyes were fastened to the table. Every swallow could be heard. Peter got up and got the morning papers and started to read. After a mouthful of dessert Ruth went upstairs.

"I don't know what's the matter with Ruth, you can't open your mouth now without her getting into a mood," Peter said.

I am now the watcher, cut and bled to watch powerlessly another's pain — a revolving tragedy.

"Peter must have an unhappy life," Ruth said, and as she had joined her life to his, why should she not have an unhappy life too? It was hard and lonely to have cast off all beliefs and safeholds the way Peter had, to have such vision, it was not easy, it made him unstable, he was impossible to live with, but he had great things to do and she flattered herself she could help him.

Oh but sometimes the towers crumbled, and where was she then? She became sick. She thought she would go mad. She wanted to die. She *alone* had no confidence in herself, but Peter gave her confidence in herself; he encouraged her to write poetry, he criticized it for her, told her when it was good and when it was only pretty or a waste of time. And perhaps it was weakness in her character, but she was nothing alone, she needed someone, and she needed someone to need her.

But oh when her towers collapsed she didn't care. She couldn't put flowers in her hair, or decorate herself, or make up her face. The bottom dropped out of the world. She hadn't the heart to live. She went about grey and listless, as she had these last few days.

I am cut and bled. She lies limply on the sofa. The heater scorches me but I eye it still. The physical pain gives me some relief.

I hold up my hand in the moonlight. The moon draws me like a magnet, an unbelievable globe peremptorily filling the sky. My head is uphung to it, my legs and arms dangling like marionettes.

Or it charges me and I leap like a shorn sheep.

The moon forces my mouth open, and my teeth, and enters me as I lay shaking in the brittle beige grass. Like a baby forcing the womb open, its electric globe forces open my mouth. It is in me. Then I notice how each single star in that enormous wideness had pinned me here and there, so that my blood is gathered in points. So I am strung on a clothes line, sagging only where there are no stars. One star moves in a tripping glide like a fly on water.

The moon's pulse shakes more potently than the roaring machines at the power plant. The glitter glues my eyes, not so much dazzled as bewitched. Who has been my lover like the moon or possessed my eyes? One finger goes numb. I drink the creeping cold caress. But the moon rivets me. Barking dogs, men's mumbles in adjacent courtyards, far booms as I lay spread out on the grass by the moon, taken entirely, made its element.

I record my Christmas day. I say: quiet sweetness at last. They hate festivals, but giving and getting allow the heart some flow. There was no mail. No news. No word from my mother. No word from my past lover. We talked. We read. We went into the garden. At night we dressed up. Ruth was in barbaric orange with a bone-tooth necklace. Maud tactfully but unbecomingly in a sweater I gave her. I in yellow velvet. We played tiddly winks.

Was this all? But to say this is to say nothing. Why record the facts if they signified nothing, but flowed over like atmosphere in an equable climate?

How can I know yet the diamond in the mass of ore? The present has too wild a heart-beat; it is too near; its truth trembles.

I am hiding something. Did you know? Why am I hiding it? It is not shame nor even a sacred secretiveness. It is something only the body's language can say, oiled by the sourceless tides of mysterious passion. The mind's surveys, measurements, calculations never know anything.

You can say the water did not rise, but that is no conclusion that the water will never rise. Suddenly the face flames. What can you know from peeping in at the door with an analytical eye? Am I being dishonest? What happened? It was nothing, and yet it was a new world's introduction. Softly you slip into things, but the world gives them harsh names. Tenderness sends its hands, that's all.

But the world of sensation has an experimenter's enquiry. Does this do this? Yes: the back of my neck, bitten, made my thigh quiver with gulping shock.

There was a moon as bright as daylight tonight. I could see my face in the brimming garden pool, and the lines in my palm. (Tonight, though, its electricity did not bite.)

It is hard to join the mind and the heart that overflow with sympathy to action. I can never so well love, understand, and sympathize if I become involved myself. My blood once mixed grows only contrary, fighting or wooing the seas. Passion pays for itself, but is not to be played with. It is not the webs of action I fear. But passion is too one-eyed.

But what colouring power it has! See with those flowered eyes and later again with no flowering. The world falls flat. You turn away sick from your spread-out deeds, your shrine.

This night, no overflowing insistence, only the tender gesture: "All right! If you don't want to kiss me . . . but I am always the one to kiss you!" Ah yes, well . . .

Eyes! Glance! Tongue! Come to my rescue, say the lubricating word, the harmonious terminator or continuer, overrule this shyness stuck where the throat's lump booms in the silence. Don't you see my naked mind watching? Bury it, O bury it in your fiery-coloured robes.

Not that it condemns. But it knows too much, holds back the loving arm to measure the radius. Asks, always, what next?

This is no novel. No characters are portrayed. No one develops as the pages accumulate. I am the only character. Me floundering in my own monotonous seas, other people the points, only, by which I measure my own growth. This is the wail of me and me alone.

If sometimes I seem to step aside and watch, it is a forced gesture, from hearing the Ladies' Auxiliary, "What do you do to justify your existence? Don't you ever think of anyone besides yourself?" My loyalty is to the moon, ladies, and I will knit no comfortable bedsocks.

I am the only thing I know. And even that I only see through a glass darkly from time to time, as something a great way off.

"There is a form," I said. "Art is only the realization, capture, and condensation of the *moment*, in any time, any place: a woman's head like a bird, bent, a oneness with a stone, Maud's feet like whipped but faithful dogs. Or pulling strange substitutes out of your own depths in isolated cells or lonely towers. Any moment out of a million that has pierced your heart in this little little life.

Peter has begun to measure the stars via mathematical formulae on time and space. Did he say that the fascination of scientific calculation made art seem infantile? I think so. I lie on the beige grass voluptuous with the moon. It would be too easy, I think, to pin your eye to the moon and swing off out of toehold.

The temperament of a dandelion or cosmic preservation — where does wonder begin?

Under the gloomy tent, inarticulate with the grievances hanging under the eyes. Put your thesis there! But the clouds choke. Is this a mood for hypothesis? Why are you angry? You insist on carrying those false images of me! What did I *say*? How can I remember? My memory is flooded with disharmony. My eye couldn't see a shape or my ear hear a note. They are absorbed in their inward chopping seas. Huddled with their thin arms tightly around their breasts, as if to keep in their jealously guarded sea of grievance! You detest me! No I don't! You didn't say so with words, but your actions said it clearly. No, I don't, I don't detest you. I don't like those false images of me you carry. That's all. That's all. The gloomy ball gathers impetus rolling down its one-way hill.

By the Devil's Pit, facing Popocatapetl and the White Sleeping Woman, among the rustling deadness of the desert, with my small gnawing grievance to be dissolved, resolved, I sit.

But it is so beautiful, so still. I think of the hopeless young ones who leapt to their death, falling falling, only to wake up at the bottom, not dead, bruised and battered, but not dead.

The lower mountains are bathed in gentleness, pastel vapours rise from them. The harsh white snow is on the two great ones, and they have attendant strange opaque white clouds.

The air is riotous with birds dashing in all directions, and insects loud with action. There is a patch of flowers, scarlet and trumpet-like but, as are so many things in the desert, thorny. Why is the desert thorny? Because, with scarcity, rare life needs more defence. (As thorny people cover a paucity). So Peter lives on purpose in a desert and mostly shoots forth thorns.

I have often thought of this Devil's Pit since we first visited it. It is a focus. It magnetises the imagination. Its incurving cliffs, its weeds sprouting out, its bowl-like bottom full of hurled rocks. Its fearful depth. It is stored in all its hugeness in my mind, and is used for troubling dreams, for finite things, climaxes, something ever present, menacing, but rich.

It is not so deep, really. It is the suddenness and the tangledness, the wantonness of fullgrown cactus trees. Are there thrown bodies' bones there on the indeterminate floor? The stone wall is cruel and convex, its layers defined in its cement colour. Far off, Mexico City slouches in its plain, darkly tufted with trees.

But this is an animal's world. You can feel their sanctuary. You can sink into it if you sit motionless, and the little bushes begin their otherwise unheard singing, the drone of grasses always alone, and birds' cries are signals, secret when too many steps tread. Even houseflies have a musical hum stretched to interpret the "desert that has been a desert from of old, and will continue a desert forever."

Now I am under the cedars in the shade. How rich to be alone, to expand. The love of man seems only a remedy for man: a crutch that will easily be forgotten in space. The singing trees on top of the hill are all excelsiors. From the summit of achievement how can my smile not spread to include my diminished world? How can I not now yield to the smile, being as I am at the focal point where all smiles are born.

We are in the middle of the manoeuvres to get to Acapulco, to get to the sea and sun, Ruth and I; to have some expansion of life around us, to say to life: "Step into this circle a moment." If we could escape to the sea! If we could! Eyes there to flower slowly that now leap guiltily over the tyrant's head, touching in a tearful sympathy, surreptitiously. To count the steps of the sun!

Lying on the sofa, talking of the sea and sun, like two prisoners describing dinners, gloating over menus:

"You *need* the sea."

"If I stay here I shall die. I know it. Look how I've aged in only five months!"

"What is there against it?"

"Nothing. They just don't want us to go."

"But we must. It's absolutely necessary for you. They don't need us here."

"I know they don't need us. But Peter doesn't think so."

He came in, glancing at us, vaguely the pleased proprietor.

"Oh Peter!" I said in a wheedling voice, "sweet sweet Peter."

"My darling," he said.

He came over beaming. I felt treacherous as I put my arms up to pull down his soft dough-like face.

"You're nice, Peter."

"You are a wonderful girl. But what is it? What?"

"I want a little something. But that isn't why, you're nice anyway."

His *vulnerable* face. Ruth giggling until he began to be suspicious.

"We want to go to the sea."

"Ah, well . . ." He got up. The judicious schoolmaster. He walked up and down, yes this yes that, but but but . . .

"It would be much too sudden a descent for Ruth. She wouldn't benefit from such a short stay, as you would have to come back a week at least before we leave. The sudden change of climate, too, might not be at all good for her. It would be lovely, of course. But I must think of Ruth. Some other time we'll go."

He went on and on. All reasons for *our* good, why we shouldn't go. He went out of the room without looking at us.

Maud came in, Maud the solicitous, the one always content to take a back seat, to serve. Her face, dry and juiceless, her hair always neatly inconspicuous. Always kind, sweet, passive Maud, schooled in self-denial.

"We want to go to the sea."

"There isn't time."

"You're the only one who drives the car, so you have to be here, anyway, for Peter. But we don't drive the car, and we really aren't any use."

"There's the house."

"But Ruth needs the sea."

"You'll never get a place to stay at this time of year."

She went out with averted eyes.

"What's the real reason, do you suppose?" I asked.

"Oh, egotism," said Ruth in a flat voice. "Maud doesn't want to be left alone. She's jealous to think I'd be having a good time while she had to stay here and drive the car and look after the house; and Peter's egotistic. He wants me to be here. He doesn't like to think we can bear to leave him."

"But he hardly ever notices us. If we even speak he snaps at us. He either works or goes to bed early. At breakfast he reads the paper. At the other meals he curses the world, goes over his grievances, and counts the fools and idiots he has met."

"I know. But we flatter his vanity. He likes to think we're here if he wants us: his little troupe."

But Ruth with dishevelled hair and sad colourless face was quiet and sober. She is like one in a decline these days. She answers graciously if spoken to, but her eyes are on the ground. She lies on the sofa as if asleep, and asks me to make the fruit salad. She says she is too tired.

For days, for two weeks, the silent battle. Ruth looking nearer and nearer to death, the tears more and more frequent, and the headaches and the spitting of blood.

I spoke to the tortoise-like doctor, a little busy-body woman with an independent spirit. I said Ruth's illness was a great deal psychological.

"Dear child, spitting of blood is not psychological."

"Don't you believe at all in the effect of love upon women?"

"Not at all. I get along very well without it."

"But women *need* to be loved, and that need can even destroy them."

"Nonsense! It's best to be independent. Men aren't trustworthy! Women are much better friends."

"My mother," I said, "ruined five people's lives

because of that need. She is half insane because of that need."

"Oh, there was probably some other reason, my dear. I have never noticed that it made much difference one way or the other. But let me tell you this. Don't have an affair with a man if you want to marry him. Men are not to be trusted. Don't ever expect a man to marry you if you have an affair with him first."

This busy and independent creature of sixty is a curer of the world's ills, with no knowledge of love. Love, or a lack of love, that twists the world and rules both heaven and hell. I left her in my despair. But she promised to tell Peter that Ruth needed the sea. She had a tremour in her voice. She wanted to talk on. I felt I was disclosing the facts of life to a surreptitious schoolgirl.

So, later, Peter sheepishly said, "I have decided to send Ruth to the sea, to see if that will do her any good. So, Betty, if you still desire to go, I should be very grateful if you would accompany her."

"Yes, with pleasure," I said, lowering my head, and smiling hilariously into my fruit salad.

The night before we left he came down to my bed to say goodbye. He walked about the room buried in his smooth dough-like face. His lower lip shoots out when he is self-conscious, like a knee in a trouser adjusted.

"Have you still a drop of sympathy for me?" he said, appealing to my latent motherhood, in his soft repentant way.

But my motherhood's compassion my mother herself used up with her orgies of hysteria. It was a great tidal sea. But now it is dry. I took her vanity for true pain, suffering more than she, but his shall not be washed in my tears.

"I know I have a bad character, irritable, hard to live with, but I have so much work, and I have wanted you so much. You *know* that, you know it, don't you? When I met you before I was sick for a week after you left. You make me desire you so, and so I am cross and enervated when you are around. I am jealous! You are a siren."

He fumbled sheepishly. He knelt down by the bed and laid his head across my breast. Like stone I lay. Then I stroked his hair.

"I am thirty-five," he said. "It is the time in a man's life when he must do some work if he is ever going to. I *must* get something done. I have a vision of what I want to do, something precise, exact, perfect. I think now at last I can do something. Do you understand? I think you understand."

What I understood was his fumbling hands, his hesitant lips like an adolescent's.

"Betty!"

The clouds, the rising tides flooding the ears, the eyes, the mind, melting all, dissolving all in my bed. But I lay like stone. I wanted to melt. Something rose to meet him. But I focussed on other images. ("These fools! These idiots!") Insinuating motherhood said he is sick! He says and does those harsh things because he is sick! He needs love! He needs understanding! Treacherous maternal instinct bound in bowels, sightless, mindless, eager to give birth and blood! But I will not be deceived. I was a mother to my mother. I am scarred with my passionate sympathy, my abortive tenderness, and I will not yield.

"Betty! I want you so!"

"I have made a promise."

"Bourgoise!" he said, "Christian! A promise! I thought you were more intelligent than that. It is only feelings that count. Those idiotic ideas of the Christian bourgeoisie! A promise! Who is ever to know?"

"And Ruth?"

"Oh, Ruth is not like other women. She understands these things. I hope you are not so foolish as to tell all you do?"

"No . . . but the webs of action?"

"Little simpleton! That's the Christian idea again! As if anything you do affected your after life! As if "pureness" existed! You surprise me! You really do! I expected more from you!"

"Perhaps it isn't that," I said, "but females, even animals and birds and insects have an uncontrollable instinct to run away from the male. We can't help it."

"Well," said Peter, "I have reached the age in life where I want to have women come to me. I don't want to chase them. I don't want to take them brutally."

"Don't you know that women *want* to be taken brutally?"

"Of course. But I want to dominate in a subtler way. I want them to be drawn to me, irresistibly, because they can't help themselves."

His white ineffectual hand fumbling; his self-revelations at once disarm and disgust.

All the longings of the weak move the mother. But I was not all mother. Could I love the weakness that longed for tyranny? Such sentimental indulgence makes dictators. The weak one whose compensation is killing.

"You don't know what you have done to me. My desire . . . it's terrible. Betty! Have a little pity!"

Desire! To be desired! But no. Dam the floods let loose.

"Oh Peter, please. I really don't want you."

"You are unkind! You are dishonest! You are a coward!"

Knives cutting me, thrust in my stomach, mother, woman, watcher clawing like wildcats in the bed.

And after he left my shaky legs carried me to the window where the white flower hung withered, and the moon, shrunken too, skulked insignificantly in the sky, and I went into the bathroom to be sick.

Cats howling outside the window. A white one, strung taut, just below. The sky in spots wildly streaked with pink. Then, along the edge of the purple-black mountains, that fierce Mexican yellow all along the way, red tiers floating above. The pools along the Pueblo road in the flat fields reflecting it all. The rose, the stimulant flush on the highest of the mountains as the sun touched them. Solitary Mexicans huddled in their blankets along the road, waiting for the bus. Activity beginning to issue from the untidy geometrical adobe houses.

We went miles out of our way, because there were no signs to guide us. It was cold. You could almost see your breath. Ruth sat huddled in a blanket. Maud drove, with her brow in ridges. Peter sat on the edge of his seat, saying "Ask here! Ask there! What fools! What idiots!"

The cold waiting-room. A journalist with a hat slouched over his eyes, tapping a typewriter with one finger, not giving a damn for anyone. Peter tender with us both. Maud solicitous. They kissed us, admonished us, waved smilingly. They ran smiling after us as we took off in the little aeroplane. We kept looking at each other, bursting with smiles.

Will it stay up? Can it stay up? The precarious pulley feeling. Touch a button and the elevator hurtles to the relentless ground.

Abandon the body! Say All is over! All is over but it is the same to me. Powerless, succumb. See the marvellous pattern.

Oh to dare to relish a pattern when you fear the giant's hurtling hand of death. Real elegance! The fop's parting pun! Or proof indeed that you loved the pattern best. You see, God, this was my true heart speaking!

The miraculous fields surrounding Mexico City, woven with a basket's precision, dotted with symmetrical haystacks along the stripes. The hills sharply shadowed, buff colour predominant. A tinge of pink. Far-off purple hills. The fields of earth dark, but dusted over, as if they had been sprinkled with cinnamon.

But it is a *mineral* country, even from a bird's-eye view. You can never kiss the earth. The best you can be is covered with dust. The ground will not receive you. It flies up dryly at your approach. No soft patch even to soothe your foot in the enduring desert.

We passed the great snow mountains and the tumbled volcanic bowls. Some bowls were cultivated inside, hidden, private fields. As we descended it got warmer, and the green more vibrant.

Rust gashes, and roads cut like a sore, narrow, winding. Then heat at last! We looked at each other smiling. Our smiles were too big. We held each other's hand, looking out the window opposite ways. When we saw the beautiful Pacific stretched unbearably broad and happy, we laughed unheard in the machine's roar.

The bay, basking below, the long wide pale beaches, the warmth! The little town expanding warmth, tropical smells, palms, flowers.

"Ruth! You are beautiful already!"

"So are you!"

"You dazzle me."

"You are blooming like a tropical flower!"

We beamed. We skipped down to the sea.

O the well-being! The freedom! Waves that break, that really break. Joy! The enormous sea's rhythm quivers like a jelly, and men within themselves have a sea that never finds its moment of foam. Oh the boiling-over, the curdling of the sea's burst! No wonder the men with their shoreless seas that have no outlet find release in that.

Be sea, be sand, be the sun's mistress. Let the wind's hands and hair be your hands and hair. Inside and out. Keep no single resistance back. Urge the rhythm to their rhythm till the rhythms beat in tune — a sustainable tune, though so wildly happy!

Peering, peering into womanhood, grasping new worlds, pliable like seaweed, stretched and floated. Dissolvable ropes connect Ruth and me. I stare upwards, trying to keep my image focussed.

The next night, lying under the innumerable stars, Ruth lay with her head cushioned on my thigh, embracing a new-found lover. I felt nothing for myself but a strange and privileged position, to watch human behaviour. Should I look at the stars in anguish crying traitress? I look at the stars but say: How many there are! And my lovely Ruth lying with her new-found lover! My benevolent thigh breathed peace like a grandmother's bosom, proud to be of use. And I listened to the dark sea pounding among the rocks and said, "This night is beautiful!"

A Mexican boy with a lantern came and tortured two sea-shell creatures, hurling them to the sand, or putting them on top of each other to fight. He squatted in his ring of light, intense in his sadistic operations, smiling, saying nothing.

The boring friend of Ruth's lover sat beside me, tried to do as his neighbour did, not because he felt the urge, but more so as to miss nothing that was going. He told his sordid story of his loveless wife, and his one desire, security. So I said, "Shall we go in?" And my cramped thigh moved painfully and I said goodnight. But Ruth and her lover, absorbed in their magical circle, didn't even hear us go.

In bed, lying alone, suddenly a cock crew like a woman shrieking, and I sprang up with a start, feeling suddenly the bed like cold sand under me, and the heavy treacherous air of the night. Ruth, whose life-hold was a hair's-breadth, deserted, undefendable in the unknown places! But night risks were only risks, while love-making was breath to Ruth. She said so too. I must believe in love. Another cock answered, barnyard and reassuring.

When Ruth came in, with tender whispering, a black and white cat came in too, and she bent over me smiling and kissed me. And I slept, as after a storm.

"Sometimes," Ruth said, "I wish I were an intellectual woman, ambitious and hardworking. Certainly it would be a lot better from most points of view. Only, there isn't the slightest hope I could be. I am an incurable animal. If I write or paint, it is only a way of decorating my cage. I am positive I'd cease to exist if I were no longer loved or desired. And I don't regret being so passive, because, like this, listening and waiting, two motionless silent bodies speak to each other, respond, and summon a presence, invincible, immortal, so that there is only the presence, and no longer two bodies, strangers to each other. The nights of sleeplessness are terrible, the anguish. I can't eat, I can't ever be at peace. But love is life to me. The only thing in the world that matters."

As I listened I held my breath; it was so precious, I was so afraid the least movement might stop her and I would lose forever those revelations I so desired.

Ruth lay on her bed talking, her eyes cast down, her life pouring out, like a cascade of water.

"When I was three," Ruth said, "I fell down stairs. They thought it was nothing, and put some salve on my thigh. But later they found it was broken, that there was tuberculosis in the bones, and I was in a cast up to my armpits for six years. When I got up, one leg was six inches shorter than the other. I was so ashamed. I could never get used to it. I always thought of myself running or even flying. I didn't want to go anywhere. I didn't want to be seen. Luckily, though, when I was ten, it was on my birthday, I was riding one of those little scooter cars, and I fell again and broke the other leg, and was in a cast again. When I got up there was just a half inch difference in the two legs. That was lucky. For I think I should have died if I had stayed the way I was at first."

"As soon as I was old enough I had a lover and of course as soon as I had a lover I became pregnant. I adored my mother and it would have broken her heart to know I was going to have a baby, and I didn't want to tell anyone. Then, six months before it was born, my mother died, and my father married again. I never told him, of course. I hated him and the woman he loved. I went away to Paris and had the baby. He was a little boy. He looked like me. He had black hair and long fingers, beautifully formed. But it was a difficult birth. I am not built like most women. The doctor said I should never have another child. He was the wrong way up and had to come out feet first. It was terrible, *terrible*. I wouldn't go through that again for anything in the world. The most frightful, frightening torture imaginable. Why? Why should such things be? It is still a nightmare to think of even. I was only sixteen. Nobody knew. I didn't want them to know. Certainly not the baby's father. But they injured his head, somehow. If they had taken proper care it would have been all right, but nobody bothered. He was quiet and he never cried much. It was a wonderful and terrible experience. I had to work to get enough money to support him, so I put him in a home. I used to come and see him every Sunday. But one day when I came the nurse met me at the door and said, "Lolly's dead," and I went in and saw him dead. He was nine months old, my son. He would be fifteen now. But I am glad he died. I wouldn't want the responsibility of making another human being go through what I've gone through. No one has the right to bring another into the world to such suffering. I am glad my son died!"

She wept with her words, and I wept too.

She talked on. Her years of working. Her lovers. Her pity for a cripple whose mistress she became and who tried to kill her when she left him, hiding the revolver under the pillow when he was making love. She had had four abortions, all painful. She hated the man when she became pregnant. She hated all men then. She didn't want to see anyone. And for nothing on earth, *nothing*, would she ever go through birth again. Peter had brought her peace and security. He had understood her. He had said, "Come with me and let me take care of you. You will never have to worry again. I will protect you." And he had been wonderful. He had been the best thing in her life. He had given her another sort of liberty. He had freed her from all the ghosts of her frightful childhood and adolescence.

"I don't think anyone else could have revived me, renewed me, the way he has, with his great love, his intelligence, and his goodness. Sometimes, as you know, he can be intolerable. But I can never forget what he has done."

She came over to my bed slowly, almost shyly.

"What impression does it make on you to know I have had a baby?"

"How do you mean?"

"Does it not disgust you?"

"On the contrary. It only makes me think how much I have missed not to have had a baby too at sixteen."

Then her smiling face, bending over me with the falling hair. I listening, listening, gathering the rare essence, waiting for the full revelation.

Her eyes, though — she was *all* woman. She was womanhood. Her eyes then were worn, tired, sad, deceived, full of bitter knowledge, love, all the wonderful and dreadful things that ever came to woman. Her eyes like this, naked, were my mother's eyes, terribly terrifyingly near — eyes my mother had after her long scenes of hysteria and crying, of pacing up and down the veranda, wailing in her uncanny voice, "I am going insane! I am going insane!" or moaning as she lay soft and whale-like in a lump on the bathroom floor.

But all the while that Ruth's naked eyes peered at me, her smiling dream mouth floated above me like the moon, smiling, smiling, tender and soothing and sure, the lips of wise love, knowing their rewards, but insinuating, like a snake, and poised ready to strike.

Ruth standing at the bathroom door, quite naked, with her hair rolled up on top, reciting two poems by Baudelaire. It was a poised moment and I said to myself: Cut this into the brain! Nothing could be richer! It is a divine accident, no one but gods could plan! She was having a shower, and I asked her a question about a poem and she came to the door to answer me, and began it, and then went on, carried by it, vibrating to it, standing like a dancer, her hands, too, in the poem. And I lay, immoveable electricity, watching.

Ruth, born of the marriage of a diamond and a seaweed: Ruth in the sea like a fish, swimming for hours till she became all blue, her eyes red and watery, her hair dank, till she was all seaweed and her diamond gone. In the water she ran and she flew, she was that angel-bird she desired to be. For the land was her suffering-post, only the water was truly her element. Sometimes she wouldn't come back at all, and the sea beating the rocks along the shore beat fear into my veins, waiting restless and apprehensive, knowing at last the drowning-pull of the fisherman who loved the mermaid. I left her in the sea and ran from door to door in search of blue cotton for a dress. But it was no fun. I was full of forebodings. As at the family unheavals where my mother left the table in tears, and I, laughing with nerves, tried to enjoy the special ice-cream or something which she had got for a treat for us, but which now turned poignant and went down in lumps, tasteless, in the general tense unhappiness, so all the gay things that came to meet me in those days were more jolts to my fear. I saw a man dressed as a skeleton, with a scythe, walking in the streets, and my heart kicked my ribs with an icy thump.

In the evening Ruth came back, and she said: "Ah! At last I can breathe all the way up, really breathe! Not just enough to keep me from falling to the ground. Oh what a glorious day!"

But later I heard her in the bathroom, spitting blood.

How can Ruth, who calls herself all animal, who makes love to anything loveable in sight, and knows that women are to be loved before all else, and my mother with her sexual fears hidden in her leather-bound Emerson, have the same passion-wracked face? How can the worn-out eyes, criss-crossed with bitterness and knowledge that they have been deceived, still see and desire to be the image of the tender one, smiling forgivingly at the deathblows given by the child?

Ruth's face approaches suffering and loving with the same rhythm, asking to be destroyed and eaten with ecstacy, knowing there is no joy given without torture.

Life escaping out of her hands. She grabs it dangling on the death-cliff. It escapes. She is drowning in her sobbing.

Ruth, Ruth. I will be your mother. And with the consoling kisses receive again my mother from your lips. Not to her womb again. But she into mine. I am hiding the thing that haunts me in my womb. But my womb is as large and as forgiving as the world. I walk complete and free, the giver of life.

Our room is like a sanctuary, a shadowed retreat from the dazzling sun. At night the palms murmur like water outside the high latticed window. Lying in the dark the two livid bodies breathe out the past day's sun.

"Are you awake?"

"Yes."

"Would you like to come over here?"

"Yes."

Do not be afraid. I will be your mother. I will feed you, nourish you, hold your trembling steps with a sure hold. Feed. Be at peace. Use me. The woman torn in the tangles of the forest. Lost. I hear the forsaken sobs. The great flesh unloved, each pore a starving mouth. O my mother, my little one, the anguish of the seeking mouth unmet!

We are in the erotic caves, warm, damp, fold upon fold, the caves, bigger than the mind can hold, they hug the mind, enveloping, sinking it back, burying it in rocking softness.

Or with my mouth I swallow myself and her.

It is my mother I swallow. It is the repellent flesh of my mother I embrace. The ogre is in my bed. For living pity's sake I am kissing the one I fly from. It is a wailing child. I am older than the world, older and stronger.

Pity rips, seeing the agonized need. Those flowery women with dewy faces in the morning. Those prostrate women in their great forsaken meadows, with their daisy chains, woven like Penelope's, rejected and scattered about. That coming they awaited, no more than a blind beast's bounding on the grass. Gone by! Flashed like a storm! Their little offerings unseen! They wanted to give! Their terrible urge was to give!

Why are there so many stars and why are they so cold? Why is the night so empty and so like a great black pit? All about my room, like clothes, are hung my images, they are locked in bureau drawers; when I am alone I take them out to stroke. I wove such mirages. I dare not tell you why. They are my drapery. My naked offering was too visible.

Are you happy? Are you happy? Yes, we say, weeping with an unhealable woe. The palms weep too, and in the north the pines. And the wind howls.

But my mother is in my womb.

IV

Poems from 1940

TIME LEAPS! TIME BOUNDS!

What bounds does time
Take through my planned garden.
Will the lilies survive
Or is chaos the stuff they feed on?
Or sent as a warning only
Saying, praise Him?

Who conducts this raucous symphony
Orders its pace?
The wild crescendo
Beating the heart out of place?
Who hushes suddenly the wind
Or stretches the hours of despair
Makes a rich substance
Or a poisonous gas out of air?

Time leaps! Time bounds!
The impact rocks earth's edges!
Or time lies crouched
Hiding in brambled hedges.
The dust rises
The gardener stands in dismay
The serene dream undone
The light going from the day.

TO BE OR NOT

Who worth keeping survives
Among these seven million lives?
Cluttering New York in droves?

The swallow that wins is beautiful
But here you never can tell.
The winners are proof against hell

And heaven. But tonic will not revive them
And never will they find home
They will be an easy catch for time.

And I? Though memory-prompted complain of
                          the street
Whose slap all footfalls meet
As if it were a mutual combat.

And no eye either welcomes me
Except the leering and tawdry,
Curiosity or envy.

So either I die or retire too far within
Clothe my one good in fatal sin
Whose wall is invulnerable against the ablest
                          engine.

So die, I say, as if choosing a hat
No melodrama but only that
And the water under the bridge is sweet.

Sweet and early and perpetual
And memory in its shimmering face looks well
And its ending kiss hardly hurts at all.

HOW ELABORATE THE BUILDINGS

How elaborate the buildings, the silt pretendings
Through dazzling images of distraction and then
                              finding
A kiss at the ending.

Only O only. A long face drugs my eyes
Dropping Not Welcome signs, Signs of the Times,
                              as he says.
It's a too too terrible world these days.

Terrible. But I swim like a swan not much caring.
Take away the trappings and give truth an airing.
My love my love when will you be here?

SONG: THE SINGING SUMMER STREETS

Nothing dies, it bursts to birth
Before the requiem is half done,
Before the suitable tears are shed
Or the mourning of the underbred
Nags out its course, the death is dead.

The sighs shoot into the loud trombone
It blows so hard it shakes the earth.
The flowers in a breathless rush break through;
If one has collapsed, then out spring two,
Insatiable for things to do.

It is unnecessary to atone
For sin: he is the losing one;
With all his conjuror's cheap disguise
No geese fly north because of his lies,
No cause is lost, and nothing dies.

YOU ARE BURIED

You are buried in my pillow of fever
And burn heavily in my eyeballs. Your odour
Pervades my bed, and will not be laid.

Though you offer me an orphan future
Which I leave untouched on an unknown doorstep
Medicine is the touch of your lip.

If you called as you do call from the bottom of the
                               sea
I would hear you in my grave easily
I would step down to join you happily.

Brushing the lies aside I shall leave my bed
I shall find you under the Rumanian dead
Under the wreck, still arched for attack.

WHAT SERENE LAND

What serene land is offered to my eye
But I would straddle it with your thigh
Arched for attack? And though too deep
That thrust for me to live can I cry stop
When the wound it bleeds is my only hope?

Winter shelters spring for action
Perhaps you are an unknown gardener
Watering seeds you plant in plotted days
Where there are no focals but your eyes.

Hope and Europe die behind your head.
But I still holding you hold a world
Ripe with unwritten history, to be beguiled
And even now big with child.

BY THE GAS JET

Here I sit who am no wizard
Courting hazard
By the gas jets to keep my eyelashes dry.

And I say cold womb be vocative
Guide the blind.
But no message reaches the hibernating I,

Drowsy as a bear. Nor will it hear
What even dreams forbear
To ignore: Four corpses in the snow. How long
Have they been there? I asked. Four months.
See their stiff mouths.
Are they angels? Were they done wrong?

Their lips are wet with dew sticky as stamen
It is an omen
Shall my child rise out of this cave of snow?

It is the eery tides bring such debris
From hidden seas
Not blood, what is this poisonous flow?

Not blood not tears not semen,
Doomed women,
It is the riddle that will rid you and breed you.

I am riddled with bullets but my will is unwritten
Ceremony forgotten
It is the need freezes me. The need the need.

EXPEDIENCY

The intensity of the wish
Was it a sharp protection against too many looks
Disintegration from violation because the mob
                saw?

On my mountain a house is
With a yellow door and The Pulley written for
                cheer
At the climb's end. But it is all ended, the house is
                sold.

To whom? Who but the acquisitive eyes
Who hate the unmean the successful the careless
                look
And said "While you listen to the birds I make the
                hay."

Expediency now eats blueberries on my hill
The damned are sipping tea with gossip in the
                tabernacle's heart.
What sanctuary to you remains undesecrated?

POEM ADVISING ACTION

With graceful strategy the circling hawk
Whips my circling sorrow to dive and strike;
Indiscrete for action the poison oak
Thrusts up her flushed face into attack;
Lizards and herbs and flowers admonish me,
Strict in their innocence: I am cowardly.
Nor will the mourning-dove condone my fault
Who breasts all hazard for a humble scrap
And when she coos courts punishment. My guilt
Is obvious, and I cannot escape.

I'D RATHER MARRY A YOUNG MAN

The embryo in the elderly man
Cries out to the dry mammalian gland
But only a devil in the bed
Satisfies a woman's need
Only archangels understand
The less as well as more than human.

O needs that pity urges toward!
O pity urged to kill the need
Of self-survival! Mothering like a map
Beneath wherever you walk is spread
All lovers sporting in her lap
Unable to gambol past the embryonic cord.

My heart and the earth and the stars and the sun
Lurch out of their course an anguished inch
To hear their senile infant cries
A man must suckle before he dies,
Be persuaded, before the avalanche,
That what he has *not* done is not sin.

But oh but oh these comfortable lies
Blare out their falsehood in the gales
When the earth and the stars and my heart and
                                    the sun
Revolve because of what they have done
And leave in their dizzy course such trails
Of glory as planets and daisies.

ESCAPING WORDS

Words, my horses, roam unbroken
In my head, or, tethered,
Wait their wandering master's ride.

They eat grass. They graze.
Or grow fat, but will never win the race
Nor be mythology's beasts;

Adoring with stampedes
The cats and hay rioting with the day
Necessity supplies them on the haphazard wind.

Their manes are braided with care
And, silver-shod, their gallop
Resounds like triumph drums,

Or incites armies and insurrection. But never
Brings them to me to be
Ever and forever carried into the home of my
                              poem.

V

New Poems

OLD WOMAN, FLYING

Why shouldn't an old woman fly?
The Duchess of Bedford amazed in aeroplanes.
But it's flights of fancy I'm thinking of, I
Feel fancy still tickling beloved epitomes.

> Old Mr Yeats
> Reached new heights
> Contained his rage
> Against old age
> And caused the best poems to be won
> When he was a very old person.

So much the better if he couldn't get it up.
When energy's oozing you should cherish each
                              drop in a cup
Until enough is gathered for a celebratory draught
To share with contrary Muse. Nothing is, aft

> er all, too late
> If you don't insult or hate her
> (and he never did)
> Why should she not recur?
> He was her friend:
> Was it likely she'd desert him towards the
>   end?

So, pale and pendulous on my shaky bough
I get ready for take-off, jeered by hoi polloi.
But wait! watch! follow with eyes, mind,
(There are so many things far better left behind)
And then like a good bird-watcher you just might
See useful manoeuvring in this late flight,

> A hello, a hooray,
> A greeting along the way
> A well, well, then
> So it can be done:
> An instigatory vesper
> In a setting sun.

ROSE DIED

Unstoppable blossom
above my rotting daughter
Under the evil healing
bleeding, bleeding.

There was no way to explain
the Godly law: pain.
For your leaping in greeting,
my failure, my betrayal,

shame for my cagey ways,
protective carapace;
blame for my greeting leaping
over your nowhere place.

Spring prods, I respond
to ancient notes that birds sing;
but the smug survivor says this is *after* the
                                    suffering,
a heavenly lift, an undeserved reward.

Your irreversible innocence
thought heaven now, and eternal,
was surprised, overwhelmed
by the painful roughly presented bill,

the hateful ways of the ungenerous.
But, loving the unsuspecting flower
could love urge bitchiness
as a safe protective covering?

O forgive, forgive, forgive,
as I know you would,
that my urgent live
message to you failed.

Two sins will jostle forever, and humble me
beneath my masked heart:
it was my job to explain the world;
it was my job to get the words right.

I tried, oh I tried, I did try,
I biked through gales,
brought hugs, kisses,
but no explanation for your despair, your desperate
                                        Why.

With its smile-protected face
my survival-bent person
is hurtled on by its nasty lucky genes,
its selfish reason,

and greets the unstoppable blossom
above my rotting daughter,
but forever and ever within
is bleeding, bleeding.

ALICE

Alice
you must keep open
a place
for things to begin.
Their flying around,
their tapping at an old wound,
show
how urgent they grow
to enter you.

They might come
they may have come
when all was closed,
shut, dark,
cold —
(they die in the cold);
even extravagant seeds
with millions of siblings
spare
cease on the concrete street.

IN THE WHISPERING HELLS

In the whispering
hells of Academe
I pussyfoot around.
Are you anti-doting
at my side,
Virgil? Dante?
as I nose out
places where they file
passion, cross-
referenced
for sometime use

Assail, or sob,
or scream a battle cry?
There she goes mad or drunk
they'll say.
Sad heart,
Indignant mind,
trying to restrain distain
for a better way —
If they should speak?
If I reply?
This hope dies every day.

POOR CAGED CANADIANS

Poor caged Canadians
Drinkless or drunk
the emotions dozing below
or errupting like burst radiators
ruining the car,
breaking the journey,
obscuring the destination:

Stand fast in vastness —
there's enough of it! —
buried in blizzards
if need be,
keeping the sweet
communion that makes a man
fit into his body like a
precious event,
a perfect treasure,
or a germ
hold the beginning
after the scary end.

A BELL

There's a new bell on my door
It will ring as never before.

There's a new fish on my hook
It's giving me an old-fashioned look.

Unconscious says it's good to eat.
Conscious says it looks like dirt.

Wily fishermen must be prepared
For novelties, old boots, even to be ensnared.

The new bell's up. It's ready to ring.
My God! But it's almost evening.

No sound. It must be Early Closing Day.
I thought you said to take the hard way.

Maybe I got confused. Most ways are hard.
(And frozen today). Could I have not heard?

Don't come. Don't ring. Unless you're the real
                              McCoy
Rushing to open to duds I should certainly not
                              enjoy.

I'll wait (the greater part of wisdom, life
And fishing) the eternal *motif*.

But I'll get my greeting ready and I'll cook my fish
Today might just be the day that I get my wish.

O POOR PEOPLE

Let us invoke a healthy heart-breaking
Towards the horrible world,
Let us say O poor people
How can they help being so absurd,
Misguided, abused, misled?

With unsifted saving graces jostling about
On a mucky medley of needs,
Like love-lit shit;
Year after cyclic year
The unidentified flying god is missed.

Emotions sit in their heads disguised as judges,
Or are twisted to look like mathematical formulas,
And only a scarce and god-given scientist notices
His trembling lip melting the heart of the rat.

Whoever gave us the idea somebody loved us?
Far in our wounded depths faint memories cry,
A vision flickers below subliminally
But immanence looks unbearably; TURN IT
                    OFF! they hiss.

HELLO

Hello Hello
From the depths of the well.
But can you hear me
When I'm so low?

I'm prowling in a cave
Deep underground
So my words might have
An inarticulate muffled sound.

I'm hacking through
Deep frozen matters
And they give off gasses
not very nice for lads and lasses.

But I see you there
Wrestling with your muses
Trying to light bombs
With burnt-out fuses.

I know you're wooing
The treacherous word
Trussed-up with feelings
And tired of being unheard.

How kind you are
To sit quietly there
Not raising a shout
And giving me the benefit of every doubt.

I feel for your wounds
Your wasted spirits
Your misplaced pride
Your unregarded merits,

I'm loving your loving
Admiring your courage
Even respecting
Your camouflage,

Your necessary mask,
Your hopeless job,
Your giving to Oxfam,
Your singing robe.

So I say Hello
From the depths of the well
And they lie who say
This love is apocryphal.

SLIGHTLY RHYMING VERSES FOR
JEFF BERNARD'S* 50th BIRTHDAY

My Dear Jeff,
I can't say enough
how much I admire
the way you have
conducted your entire
life, and the way you have
used your marvellous Muse.
And how right she was to
choose you. Because
she's a Rare Bird who would
have retired or died
if you hadn't known how
to amuse
her, and her you.
That's one non-bogus
marriage made
on Parnassus
and *true*.

She knew
exactly what and who
she was letting herself
in for: the real You.
Drink, betting shops and pubs
are the sort of thing that rubs
her up the right way:
she'll always stay
and make you more beautiful
and witty
every day.

*Jeff Bernard is a British writer who writes a regular column,
"Low Life," for *The Spectator*.

This is a loose love
Ode, owed
to one of my friends
who is in my special
collection of people
who make amends
for endless excruciating
boring hours
so often lived
when foolishly pursuing
stimulation,
and none occurs.

Sterne, Benchley, Leacock,
Carroll, and Nash, and Lear
are not more dear
to me than bedrock
Bernard (3).
(Do I not pay 65p.
ungrudgingly weekly,
for a fixative laugh,
uniquely Jeff?,
who has become
a consolatory
addictive to me?)

Wilde would have smiled
and been beguiled
and bright enough to know
that *you* had a better
Muse in tow
than he.
Could he see
the angelic emanations
from gutters where we
all fall, while
trying to pee,
and rise, or try to rise,
unwisely, in majesty?

And Swift is bitter
and cross
and doesn't make us
feel better
at bearing our lot,
and, in his rage
at the odds,
misses the old adage
that recurs to me
often, in every mess:
"against stupidity
even the gods
are helpless."
He
lifted furious fists
but had no effect
on the jibbering idjits.

Your subject is not mean,
who's up, who's in,
or jockeying for position
(what a dreary sin).
Funny but kind,
your subject is justly seen
as the inexhaustible one
of nude mankind:
Yourself, in fact, drinking,
amidst the alien corn,
and explaining the amazing joke
of being born.

Your sources —
grief and love
and the Coach & Horses
and all the things we're
thinking of
but don't admit,
because they don't fit
our grand ideas of
our own importance.
You hit the
soul on the head
when it rises
out of its lying bed,
pompous with portents
above its station,
and greedy for rewards
above its ration.

But you're never snide,
and you never hurt,
and you wouldn't want to win
on a doctored beast,
and anyhow the least
of your pleasures
resides in paltry measures.

So guard, great joker God, please guard
this great Bernard,
and let 1982
be the most brilliant year he ever knew.
Let him be known
for the prince of men he is,
a master at taking out of
himself and us the piss.

If you will do this, God,
I'll be good all year,
and try to be better-dressed,
and soberer, and keep my prose-style clear,
(for this great man
is embedded in my heart)
I'll remain, Sir, then and only then,
Yours sincerely, Elizabeth Smart.

ALL I KNOW ABOUT WHY I WRITE

My poor blind passion wells up, though
forced by expediency sometimes to hold its
                    tongue.
Some saw an appalling innocence (naked
naivety). They saw with blush and *frisson*.
It reflected back.
So passion crouched, crouches.
So, squashed, fights feebly back.
It can't *not*.
The message is like the one in the genes.
It *can't* be disobeyed.
(O flagging prizefighter, lurching from bloody
                    corners —
there's game for you!)

To examine this tottering passion?
What, whence, why, whither?
Measure and weigh it?

I think not.

Men and boys delight in diverting caterpillars
from their destination.
They laugh. Why?
It's the dogged orientation that again and
                    again
insists on its original destination.

This poor pre-butterfly I see in me, this
                    caterpillar
passion, balked but cocky, is the pet I must
                    protect, feed,
understand the needs of. (Needs must, when the
                    devil drives.)
This caterpillar is not masked — how silly
                    can you get? —
he's naked as a drop of water. He has no shell, no
                    pupa, no cocoon.
His necessary helps are delicate, subtle, require
                    domestic angels
to cater to his needs. His habits are not heretofore
                    known; and
his destination is blurred.
        I talk in riddles. I'd rather speak plainly.
        But some ways are still unmapped.

        Yes, every morning, when light reflects
in the West (can't see the East), the unsquashable
urge arises, wobbling its unseeing hopeful head
about — is this the day? at last? now?
        It's embarrassing to harbour such a worm;
to go so unclothed among the gossiping of the
                    concrete world:
a slow organic matter moving over the plastic
                    palaces
in a ridiculous search for an unknown destination.
        But this happens, most days of the week.

Disobedience (what a well-packed portfolio
this word is) to *anybody's* messages from genes
breeds disaster (cancer, for instance, constipation,
coldsores, brain tumours, rhumatoid arthritis) —
the pilot must act when the antennae receive the
coded order.
Or he's a bad boy.
Not fit for his duties.
And will be fired from the Force.

(the Forces: there's another strong-armed
word innocently giving away its aims.)

Indefatigable it is, and must be, this poor
blind
passion welling up every dawn for seven long
decades.
Again and again wearily, patiently circumventing
the obstacles
(casually, or malignantly, or without a thought) laid
in its way.
When stunned, though, lying doggo, shocked
or asleep,
till the weather turns clement, and the winds drop.

It's not really my business to watch
or analyse this wiggling; only to tend the worm.

But I thought you'd like to know.

VI

In the Meantime: Diary of a Blockage
(January – April, 1979)

19 January: Rather cheerier today, with soft snow covering everything, adding brightness. But cold.

I did the ironing.

20 Jan.: Millions and millions and millions of large wet soft white flakes falling.

Bartok clinking.

26 Jan.: A thicker whiter blanket. Amazing white landscape, only criss-crossed with grey tree-trunks and branches. A canopied light. Subdued but bright.

2 February: Phone off. Pipes frozen. Roof leaking in three places. Too icy for moped, and anyway I have to wait in case telephone men come. In desperation I tried the end of John's home-made wine, but it was vinegar. One sip went through me in a sharp disintegrating way, an undermining, disrupting? corrupting? making-dissolute? way . . . disorganising? unsettling? decentralising? way . . . dissolving? decomposing?

Put moped in kitchen to warm up, so that I can start it. May have to push it through gravel pits to road.

6 Feb: The *grip* of winter. Crusty snow. Branches rimmed. The front lawn is a chaos of molehills, some exposed, some humps of snow. Slippery. A cheerful sun emerging after early mists.

Valentine's Day. A terrific blizzard and strong NE wind . . . and the snow went on and on and on and it is now and as white as ever. Under the oak and the Judas tree there are some desperate peckings about in the exposed ground. An excursion in the blizzard from Shadow Barn: defeat, failure, collapse.

15 March: Concentrate on one point.

Blocked even to write about blockage.

Troubled shrubs.

It's a terrible place, where I want to go. You'd have to repudiate every kind of human love, especially the mother's.

I want to go there.

But this is not to say I don't need human love: various sorts are essential to survival.

How can I commit the dastardly act of going down to that dark place while soliciting the comfort for when I come back?

Nature makes mother love, parental solicitude, for the going-on of the species. Perhaps passion comes under this heading, too.

God is not involved in this, anymore than he is in who sleeps with who or how. Is this not clear?

What I want to explore is the severance, the necessary severance, of this wonderful completeness — in the womb, perfect, and even for many years after — a passionate connection.

No problem for the birds — off they go with never a sigh on either side.

I'm tangled up in the various layers of the Mother thought. From pretty and superficial to deep, ugly, murderous.

The smug mother love walking around so self-congratulatory, so sure it won't be shot-at. Sacred, known to be sacred, scaring the jeerers, touching the toughies, committing acts of super-egotism under the guise of unselfishness, and with the approval of the world.

Oh but we were so cosy. We were all-in-all to each other. A total understanding.

"Mum? Mum?" I heard the young woman cry out in her sleep.

Forty years later the cry is worse, more agonized, bereft.

And the orphans' dreams? Worse. An obsessive theme. A searching hunger. A wishful wondering.

A useful lack of acquaintance with the demanding facts, the unglamourous prickly possessiveness that lies out of sight.

Is all this really troubling me? Or is it only a stage on the long way down, superficial compared with the black holes of energy . . . a simple sample of the Garden of Eden?

Hubris: wanting to walk and talk with God, instead of getting on with the gardening?

Collapsed in on themselves (but is collapsed the word?) and condensed to a millionth fraction of their former selves; but powerful powerful, drawing in with overwhelming suction, and able to give out HOLY energy?

and before that? and before that? and before that?

I'm glad, this year, that I had the Motorway experience, the Blizzard experience: a slapping back to total helplessness in the face of the rude forces.

"Confidence appals."

Then where will the energy come from, the confidence to step, see, speak?

I didn't need to be told that I was growing old, weaker, frailer, huffing-and-puffinger, hopelessly unable to keep up with a ten-year-old child on the run.

I'm sorry, this year, that I had to come in contact with mean minds, ignorance, ignobility. I should like to have remained, or been able to go, back to being, "all gloriously unprepared for the long littleness of life," and have kept on imagining intelligence, kindness, insight, wit, in every travelling scholar, a noble curiosity in everyone who takes an interest in the arts. I knew this was impossible: I have catered to the world's veniality and vanity since I was teenage, but my knowledge then was theoretical, and I always thought there were many dazzling exceptions. Perhaps there are. I still assume everyone knows more than I do until it's blatantly obvious that their chase too had a beast in view.

This is far far from conceit. Where would I find conceit? I long to be corrected by the haughty gods. But the vandalous facts, however one mulls them over, turn out to be vandalous facts. Kicks from the ignorant cannot be confused with a knucklerap from the headmaster. Slow work, proving to yourself what you knew in the beginning but didn't want to believe, in case, in case, in case . . .

Confusion often arises from being so impressed by the things other people know or can do and I don't or can't: i.e. understand internal combustion engines, cuts of meat, the theory of relativity, how telephones work, how to set bones, how to administer a catheter, how to make a speech, sing, act, administer, do shorthand, add, brew, develop photographs, fly an aeroplane, diagnose meningitis, strip a cupboard, saw, paint, make woodblocks, teach, cook meringues, pot, camp in the antarctic, drive a lorry, tolerate housework day after day, speak arabic, tailor, lay out newspapers, type-set, be a plumber, mend a television set, bind a book.

Boo hoo. I'm not feeling self-pity because I can't do any of these things well, or at all. But someone who can disarms me and impresses me and wonderful technological knowledge could easily be mistaken for intelligence or wisdom — not that these might not be present as well.

Give up expecting every vicar to have an insatiable passion for God.

How boring that was.

And it gets us nowhere.

The small rain is whirling every which way, criss-crossed, fine, undirected, blown by two winds or more? Some of it is almost snow.

The plants, now lying so fallow, except for the small force of the little bulbs, get their big irresistible force in May. Where from? The sun? Where will mine come from if it does?

"Blindly" on. Biting nickels for falseness. Trying not to mind scoffing and scorn. "Yes, maybe you're right, but nevertheless, something tells me

. . ." ("How unscientific can you get, dear?")

Well, then, why do I sink into these mighty
SLOTHS, lasting, sometimes, months?

I saw the catatonic rats — very interesting —
one fell over as if dead or stuffed. It was in a pro-
gramme on television, about the indiginous mor-
phine in the body, and its antidote, also present,
discovered recently, because of research into drug
addicts. Which makes me think how right I was to
wonder and ponder "Whence cometh the catatonic?", but like that just to be jokey (the Bible, the
gasman) because it nags so, is so dreadful to suffer.

Bored birds.

Catatonic rats.

Euphoria hidden in a secret corner of the brain.

Analgesic and adrenalin stuffed in the body like
a good housewife's first-aid kit.

If one had a housekeeper!

If one had total control!

To take in, to let out, to use, to store.

Nature takes care of a lot of it, but, as I seem to
keep saying, she is *not* interested in art, god, in
anything but keeping the body in good working
order.

Steal the keys? We try to when we drink, drug,
stay awake to measure the speed of light, or even to
win a paltry petty glory such as a political campaign
or a pop-song contest or the rubbishy production of a
play.

It goes against the gravity.

The rhythms, the patterns of the world in all its
particles — under the microscope, in the sky — the
seasons, the cells, the waves, horticultural harmony.

Mushrooms of the secret marriage — all done underground, the sexual ceremonies, the plotting and planning — only the fruits, the results, come up and declare themselves.

If only, every day, day after day, a little scribbling could take place, the obscure design the larger purpose would emerge and the whorey horse dash off over the landscape.

The inarticulate bursts forth, unable to keep silent any longer, abandoning the boring circling round and round these everlasting sores.

The human — I can hear Rossini going on about it — and Shakespeare's poetry is woven round it — but that was long ago and had to be.

What is poetry wound round now? The sweetness and shortness and sadness of life, the inevitability of death, the beauty of the world. All these have to have humans suffering by — but they don't have to be identifiable, or their clothes or neuroses described as for the FBI — just little figures in a landscape.

The Greek Chorus?

The Heroes?

The naughty gods?

Could there be tensions without at least two people?

Yes. Such as a Holy Sonnet.

Alas, Elizabeth, you are still listening to the inane mumblings of inane people who have nothing to do with you or anything else. How mud sticks! ("ground lost", said Logan Pearsall Smith). Go down, where no sounds penetrate.

But I must keep open, must notice the omissions that make the equation.

Courage! Think of the daring feats of the ones that went before. The single-minded leap.

It's only a matter of doing it every day and being in contact in a working way with other doers so that there's no possibility of a cringing doubt (i.e. how easy and amusing it was to review books for *Queen*. How hard, how impossible to review them now for anyone).

How can you be certain and yet open and trembling as a jelly? This is the working equation. (I remember, now, I wrote of GB* that "he goes from the sheepish and shame-faced to the roar of authority." No wonder I always admired him as a worker and a phenomenon. But he has blocks too, don't forget.)

Snow like caster sugar, fine, almost invisible, contrary, from the East, from the North. Plumtree beaded in raindrops. Some plants very still, some stirring nervously.

The roar of authority rises pretty fast when other people are gabbling on ridiculously, oblivious of the point at issue ("at issue" — what does that mean? I shouldn't have used such a phrase) — full of error and self-importance.

But of course, sometimes it is impossible to intervene, amidst their noisy opinionatedness.

Protests. Protests.

Well, Person, I'm only trying to encourage you to have courage, to have confidence in your confidence.

* George Barker

A bad television play, if you can bear to watch it through, should spur you on. "You can do better than *that*," as the Taste-of-Honey girl said to herself one night and proceeded to get herself a tidy little tiny little triumph.

The well-wishers? The encouragers? They float so far away. One needs some strong devoted person (or 2) constantly at hand saying "You're wonderful! You're wonderful! You can *do* it! You can *do* it!"

But I couldn't stand having them around.

But I see how the frail disgruntled geniuses require such persons and grind them into the ground in the course of using their help, ignoring their needs, telling them, convincing them, that their greatest possible glory is to be a handmaiden to the Muse of a genius.

When I was young, I scorned such geniuses, I despised their miniscule gifts, colossal egos, out-of-touchness with the suffering of others.

But still. I see their need, now.

There must be a more elegant way of creating confidence for yourself — the safe ground on which to stand and tremble.

Now the snow blows, from the skies, from the South as well as the other which-ways; it's thicker in bulk, but not in flake, and whirls wildly.

Rossini and a bowl of squashed smashed Jerusalem artichokes companion me.

Up from the darker lower place to toy with some surface thoughts — like could I write a play for television — funny it would have to be; action it would have to have; people growing, changing? Not

139

necessarily. Pluck up all the amusement you've had here and there, the people that held you in thrall.

A message? I must be joking.

(Drops on the winter honeysuckle so large, so frequent, they look like pussy-willows, swollen to bursting.)

Very, very fast slapstick — a woman passes and repasses dragging and slapping a child.

Juxtaposition (Such as "Mother Mother my soul's on fire").

(You might explain — the laughable non-communication.)

Two elegant young men making aphorisms that just miss the point.

The soup boiling over.

The stuff in the oven sending burning fumes out in vast wafts.

Sounds like Firbank, Monty Python.

Sounds like the advertisements.

But children love the ads best and weave them into their other programmes. Fat old mascara'd lady dancing frantically to "It's later than you think."

But there must be some tears in it too.

Sounds like a skit, a revue, a dejà-vu.

But, I can't leave my post. I can't go after these things. They are in my head, they'll come to me; they have already incorporated themselves in past writing (in a small epithet I throw away another's whole life — or *collect it* — collapsing into concentration like the Black Holes). So, maybe never a play, TV, radio, or stage, only, as usual, a distilled sentence or two, with the plot squashed into penny size.

Why am I explaining to myself so many things I know?

140

Maybe to get rid of them — they clutter up the place, floating around inanely.

Scene in a nightclub, with cheerful lone girl quietly stripping unwatched. Men drinking, dealing, betting. Noisy man throwing off his clothes to reveal bulging belly and droopy drawers. Worried Algerian waiter and law-wary manager. Smooth chorus of laughing, composed friends contentedly enjoying the scene as if it were a cabaret.

Slap Slap Clap Clap — this sort of a motion that looks like aggression but is really cooperation.

Couldn't I get to a round table where people were trying to make up jokes? I'd be scared at first but would loosen up later under pressure.

It only took a few weeks to get the hang of advertising, and it was amusing for six months; so was *Queen*, for even longer, and *House and Garden* for a while too.

Once you take off your jacket and start to sweat and work against the clock it all starts to happen.

"That's nice, dear," said my mother when my sister said she was seeing a psychiatrist. "Did he think you were nicely brought up?"

Slow reaction. It's taken me nearly a year to realize I'm free. But I'm so poor, my actions are constricted: no car, no money, no clothes, no figure, no beauty, no energy. Still, I could rearrange things. A good piece of life to lay out as I like.

Attachments — well, I'll have to worry about my children until I die, and to a far lesser extent about my grandchildren — but does the memory of such anxieties, and in the case of sexual attachment, jealousies, desperate desires, make one avoid them, and rest in the contented cowfields of friendship? Easy affection, no one with the slightest control over me?

I'm boring myself, again. This pill seems to prefer the equable social levels. Still it keeps my hand moving — that's something. Not blockage, mere diarrhea . . .

That was nearly all ideas, and very little of the magic marriage of words which writing is, after all, what writing *is*. Ideas are two a penny, yes, but not ones I can see a faint possibility of my being able to use.

Compassion — sometimes one can't feel it, or anything. Then something opens, or melts, and it comes gushing through. So, sympathy, concern, imaginative insights into others' lives: they mustn't come too often, or they'd flow in from everywhere and drown the person, and obscure the view of the navigator. If I keep track of this one female body (mind, soul, collection of whatnots, same as everybody) and observe faithfully and truly, I'll tell all. Only a fool would call this self-absorbed, since I am trying, as much as is possible, to see what is going on, catch myself unawares, and if I listen carefully enough, I'll know which is true universal, and which is surface disturbance. It's unmistakeable, with true ardour.

Thus envy is something I can't describe from the inside, because I don't feel it, but can observe it in others — usually elaborately camouflaged, denied, inverted.

While jealousy I know all about, and how it cohabits with sexual passion, obsession; and how it is more worth the scientist's consideration.

The light fades, 5.45. Little gusts of wind. But the snowflakes have become discouraged. A damp and sinister March day, at the very end of the Great Snow winter.

Pots of miniature daffodils sit by. (*Narcissus asturyensis*, but for one rogue Hoop Petticoat).

Confidence regained?

Before, I couldn't say "I want to write."

Now, I feel hate circling somewhere around me out there.

Well, the answer to everything was, is always, ever shall be: Become stronger, be braver.

But the conflict is: the body or the work, the what-is-called meaning-no-judgement, art. What is best for one is often what is worse for the other.

Be stronger, even so. Give a fair ration of obedience to the body, then stride out and ignore the scolding clacking tongues, just trying to scare you, guard you, smother you in comfort.

(I *was* an obedient daughter to my body — but I needed it to make good babies, look after them — now that's over, but old habits die hard. *Kill* them.)

143

Before I was thirteen, food, drink, sleep, etc, never interfered. Back to where you were before this time-consuming, body-battering, emotion-wracking, soul-stealing parenthesis began.

OK. Begin again. Beated and chopped with tanned antiquity, and still dependant on an inspiration descending like lightning from Heaven. 65 down and 5 to go, or a bit more, with luck.

Old age, aging, growing old, is what I must mention, and the severing of the ties, the divesting oneself of the love of created objects which doesn't necessarily mean that it might not be healthy and hygenic mentally and physically to take a young vigorous lover, would fate bring one to hand. (Ah me, I'm not sure about this, at all, it's pride mostly, fear of humiliation, that stops me from exploring the possibilities.) It is curious, though, to be ugly, fat, not seen as a rival by others who are love-objects, even a has-been, though I never was a been — but "You've had your life: move over and give us room." "I'm still Me," say the old folks, with a timid stamp of their foot, a roguish slightly cringing coquettishness that could be knocked down with a feather.

It was never just Death, but the decay creeping from within, the horror you carry within you that hits you at the first wrinkle, and grows until it encompasses you all, and you are just a funny old bit of paper flesh that bears no relation to the earlier you.

The physical weakness — even if you are an athlete or a dancer who's never stopped exercising, the liability to chills, the need for rest, the longer lengths taken for recovery after drinking, the pride that must go, if it had any physical basis, the knowledge that time is running out and you haven't finished your assignment.

But, there are many compensations, even improvements, in old age.

I'll tell you about these later.

Now come the shivers, cold, cold, but they held off for long. Tomorrow I go to London. We'll see how it goes. I'll go for a rest, a restful evening (ah, ah, that old comfort siren — Careful!)

6 April: More large wayward wet flakes are falling. Imagine! More large wet drops beading the branches. And coldness still an inconvenience.

The *shape* of a life.

A pill too kind? Laced with euphoria. Would you be tempted to settle for euphoria? *Never*. Would you be willing to settle for an absence of catatonia? Possibly.

But is maybe the catatonia necessary, like a dam that makes things accumulate? It takes so long to accumulate enough for a statement. Millions of trimmings, but useless on their own.

It is *possible* there are people hearing me? There are tiny signs, but it seems too good to be true. Would this be a help to me? Or too much of a responsibility? O a help, I think, a help to know one was not a totally mistaken person, piling up a small heap of old rubbish. It's a heady thrilling thought to think that things *do* get through, might, *have*.

Was the Mother idea a dead-end, a mistake? Do I still scream?

This being interested in something besides yourself — true, untrue, depending on what layer you're functioning on. They never say such things about music, or talk about a musician's egomania — though he might be a bore to know, or bumpy to meet. His obsessions are recognized and applauded early (with luck). (I am listening to some Chopin — so characteristic, so seductive — what mean thing could anybody say about him? — no story, no people, no places, etc. etc. No, of course not, silly.)

One weaves around the obstacles, gets up groggily from the knocks, knows, vaguely but passionately, the shape of the life, the direction of the road, remembers all too well the pain of making, tries not to flinch, shy away.

I wasn't going to write about *my* mother — only the passionate relationship — serving nature? — longer-lingering than the most passionate sexual love — and more abused?

Some small thing.

Atwood's advice to her daughter: "Be ruthless when necessary; tell the truth when you know it."

The interestingness of growing old. But how, even more than death, far more, people don't think it applies to them. They'll always be young, strong, and have the use of all their faculties.

It's not for BULK that I need to shape one more work.

But at least I think I am beginning to shake off the jeering inhibiting voices, the slappers-down. They grow faint, thank goodness. The bruises fade. The purpose arises, the ears begin to hear.

What am I waiting for? (besides the Muse, the energy, the last-minute panic — the certain desperate dash for the winning-post)?

Windows all misty from boiling bones.

"O where's it all gone, my life?" wailed Maxie at 70.

The spirit is alive.

It hides.

It manoeuvres.

But it is strong.

Matter is flimsy and pathetic in comparison. The spirit weeps over matter and its short vulnerable moment.

(Blind Roly, the dog, sniffing the air with joy, remembering. Young Roly leaping ecstatically for so much, so rich. Wounded Roly in the santolina, in pain, reproachful, baffled, struck down unbelievably.)

"Vital feelings of delight."

First the rev-up. Then the TAKE-OFF!

"They were born; they loved; they suffered; they were pacified; they died." Did I say they were bewildered? I forget. But anyhow they *are*.

1. Sexual love.
2. Art and Survival.
3. Old Age and Death

The Mother mystery has to come into the old age part, because . . .

Because it is the mother from one's childhood; and also *being* a mother, which, while it never finishes, becomes clearer as the years go on, the grandchildren elucidate, other people speak about such matters as *their* children reach adolescence, and the halcyon years, the fatuous hopes fade.

The "love of created objects" falls away.

Does this make one feel free, *or* guilty? Love turns into compassion, compassion itself freezes stiff — if it were non-functioning because of one's affair with heaven, if one were sure of this, but can one ever be? Alas, never.

If only one could always be a sharp, vibrating functioning instrument! But even domestic electricity goes wrong, trips out, and this is much more complicated.

A cold inhospitable April day.

"As freezing persons recollect the Snow —
First — Chill — then Stupor — then the letting go" (ED*, c 1862).

Ravel is coming on, violins are revving up. Preliminary chat.

"This wound in my side" — the umbilicals coiled forever and forever — contemplate the navel? — remember the moment of severance. We were attached but separate. It's easier to abandon your children than your mother — which is the memory of a hope of perfect human understanding, a oneness of course impossible, but a vivid unforgettable leaping hope, aroused again by passionate sexual love, but even *that* is easier to get over, being never so

*Emily Dickenson

148

perfect as things were in the womb, and even, sometimes, for a lucky while after, and even when imper-
fect and cast off, still nigglingly determinedly urging
until the dreaded rival, the sibling usurper, shows
you your true position. Alone, unloved, forever.

A hopeless position — where *anybody* stands.
This moves your bad old heart, your atrophied affec-
tions. This stays your hand, when you manoeuvre
selfishly in the untried name of art, or even God,
ruthless and therefore necessarily blind (needs must
be) to crying mistakes; no time for a hygenic slap, a
tutorial, a tear, a lullaby.

Hitch a ride on these desperate cars. But they
are careening for the love of speed, mapless. Energy
so immense it is expendable.
(Lavish as dandelions afloat — millions ready to go
— what if a million or so are lost?)
             Mother! I'm flying!
             Look! I've left the nest!

But the birds are luckier: adolescent, they
know the way over the seas, they veer with their
peers, make the great journey, as ship-shape as
Cook, as safe as Darwin, the songs built-in.

"Mary Mary quite contrary" thrills generations.
Eyes sparkle with revelation, hands clapping,
rhythms joining song and dance and story.
             "What a position
             the lady physician
             was in when we got there.
             Legs in the air
             Never a care.
             Tum ti tum ti tum."

Laughter peels. Repetition delights
  "Was in when we got there!"
  "& threw him down the stairs."
Hurray! we understand.
It's recognition.

Am I really old? Am I really going to die soon?
Can these things be?
Have I said I was here?
Did you know I loved you? and you? and you?
One does communicate with people after they
are gone. Small murmured words take on their
meaning, half gestures become quite clear, hidden
things behind masks, masking behaviour, contrary
attitudes, float slowly to the surface long after graves
are overgrown, ashes scattered, letters lost.

What were the puzzles? The hardest to fathom
were the meannesses, the unprovoked aggressions,
the hits for no seeable reason, some cancerous gnawing within (but surely not simple irritation, boredom, frustration, O foolish disintegrated person?)

Now I lay me down to sleep . . .
Regret — mostly for the slow too stately way of
words spoken. (Written, they go off on their own life,
find their right time, like seeds, whirling, floating,
snapping, bursting, lying low for generations till
conditions are right. How I repeat myself! — but
only after a long circular tour — I return to the same
place.)

I tried too hard to cut through the gooey casing,
knew it had better be oblique, except at special
moments, but what a long long waste of time. Necessary? It seems so, but why is it not yet clear?

150

Poor people.

Still, there's nothing to tell, except what this breathing (still) nugget, this going-on person, this me, can tell you. What's the use of pretending you know what's going on in the other nuggets of life? (Stop it — you're answering chastisements from people who don't understand. Obliterate them — except for the large compassionate, historical why and wherefore, etc.) Interesting puzzles, probably easier to solve than you think.

O I do dread the long painful making.

A beautiful young girl asked me. "What was it like to be beautiful?"

Sometimes they almost ask me (except that they're so polite, so tentative to avoid offence) what's it like to be old?

It was embarrassing to be beautiful.

It's comfortable to be old; it's so much more forgivable.

How delicious bread is when you're hungry. (I'm not even eating the new loaves — crust from last time is all.)

And sometimes, when you're thirsty, how heavenly water is.

And sometimes, when your eyes are clear, the greenness of the grass is the height of delight.

Muse — *ou êtes vous?*

This stuff is too loose to make any bricks of. Is it any use at all? We'll see. The thing is to keep the hand moving.

Living with rats. With moles. With rabbits. With large greedy birds. With whatever obliviously gobbles up your hopes, lays waste your plans.

Is it any use to sniff around the catatonic? Would it be useful to know whence, why, wherefore about it? No, only a way out, what to do *when*. Seek to know no more.

Children.

Confronting nothingness.

But it's *not* nothing.

But it is the possibility that it might be; while believing that it's not, while admitting that it might be.

What is *is*.

What was *was*.

But after the ises and wases?

What remains in the astral swirl?

Like rubbing sticks that make the fire, two words rubbing each other give off a spark, as near immortal as trivial ephemeral civilization can produce.

i.e. Art.

Art, for a little while, gives it a shape, celebrates its beauty, articulates its pain, puts its tears to use.

"The hungry sheep look up" . . .

& Lo

Someone has been here before.

Is it just a slightly more elegant getting together for warmth, cattle close crowded in a field against enemies, storms, fear?

Can't you be contented to live with the Mystery?

Well, I danced. I was never so silly as to stop and say Why? then. It was enough, itself.

152

& then you might say the great dances live on.

Live on? A little. Not for ever. I know. Never mind.

This old person, anyhow, is driven on regardless. And was, even when a young person. It seems to be the first duty. *The* assignment. No getting to the pearly gates without your homework done.

All right. Agreed. I know. I always knew.

Is this just another roundabout procrastination? A no! no! I can't, don't make me! I'm frightened! It hurts!

It hurts? It's only a little boredom. Then comes the relief! Keep that in mind.

But these are bumpy, amorphous places to map; these are elusive elderly passions to capture; so large, so loose, to form into a shape, a seeable shape, a useable analogy.

But everyone who lives gets to these places. Unless they let their eyes glaze over they come to these bleak residues.

(Make your residence among these residues.)

"Grow old along with me
The best is yet to be" . . .

(A lie, at least too facile.)

Nag. Nag.

Snuffle round in circles.

Under the waffling, the scaffolding goes up. One hopes. Lo and behold, we can build up the walls, move in the furniture, decorate a bit, fill the larder.

Maybe.

(Here follows another little run at this nagger — early version of "What is Art? said Doubting Tim".)

153

Just handy band-aids?

(Muse! You beast! Come back!)

Keep to your own peculiar rhythms, let the rhymes lie, lie, lie, as they lie. They're not for the likes of I. They only obtrude, confuse.

Funny how Stevie and Louis MacNeice both wrote poems about The Person from Porlock at the same time. But anybody who writes does so long for these interruptions.

Why does it hurt so? Why is the absolute concentration so like a beast on your back?

Are we eating our own entrails? Is it hope of being spared before we get to the heart/arteries, and the life starts seeping out forever? A mad pursuit, and yet a longing to be stopped. Any excuse to abandon the chase.

How is it done?

(Never mind Why — why nag on about that: What is art? etc.)

HOW.

I don't feel superior to trees. I wish I knew all they know. I hope they will teach me. I contemplate them and try to learn. They are my elders and betters.

Kaleidescope — colours, shapes, move into different patterns.

Steady on, lads, steady on.

("Go easy on the butter, lads, it's forty cents a pound.")

I made notes in the storm. Seasick and all, I made notes. Now I use them (or should) to make a charm against the storm, against the seasickness.

A guidebook for travellers?

Not quite. Magic. Spells.

"From Harmony, from heavenly Harmony
. . ."

Frolicking all around, I am.

Gusts, wafts of delight occur: a white oval of snowdrops across the grass lifts my spirits suddenly, uproariously.

The old cosiness comes, too, encircling one from the surrounding gloom.

"What I tell you three times is true."

But I find myself repeating things I said 40 years ago, coming upon them huffing and puffing laboriously, again, again, finding them — but they were never lost.

I think I speak clearly enough.

But there is, isn't there? something new, something more to say? Yes, but the frame's the same. The seasons roll round. The birds sing as day breaks.

O how beautiful.

O how long — but how short it seems.

Tie up these teasing balloons bobbing about your head, make a big beautiful bunch — and then?

Prepare a place to put them.

Would I, could I, budge without a purpose?

Without art or god?

But it takes great strength to be a hedonist, to be interested enough to find the game all-absorbing.

Some people do?

You'd have to keep a tight hold of vanity, ego, ideas of intellectual splendour (already touching art), insatiable curiosity, gluttonous greed, unending lust (but it *must* end), infantile ambition.

So you see, my dear, how the world wags. I do. Would you wish these things away, then? I wouldn't dare. Who am I to say?

Only, I say, *not* for me, please.

What kind of passion is it that still inhabits me? Caged, but nosing around, nudging me, saying, Let me out!

I can't let you out, P, until I have a place where you may safely graze. Then you shall be my own true free-ranging Passion of the later years.

Build your yard, then make your frame. Passion wants out. What then, then? I won't be emptied then. Another grows, grows, gets to the time of greatness, wants to get out and go too.

None of your business.

Only the business in hand.

Why am I off (or almost) the Mother frame? I talked too much? I hustled myself, was hustled? It doesn't matter. It does.

Before you see the end, you can't begin. Even writing the silliest article this was the rule. The first sentence contains the end, knows exactly the length, the ups, downs, surging centre, climaxes achieved, subsided. Of course, of course, the shaping spirit. I know.

Calm down. Rev up. A combination of both: the calmness holding down with firm determined hand the revving raring-to-go wildcat urge.

Yes, but the place, the building. The brain-work, the paperwork, the legwork.

Type. Scissors. Paste. Start again. Begin again Milligan.

Fade away, fade away, friends, and when you are faint enough, the ink almost illegible, they come

156

along to disinter you, less than whole, now, hardly resurrectable. What's this then? Even notes on the battlefield itself are hardly enough for the full flavour.

How wonderful that a times' lies do fall off like old scales, the fashionable attitudes, equivocations, prevarications, dissemblings, deceits, snobberies, prejudices — they wither up, fly away — ALL IS EXPOSED.
And it doesn't take long.
(One of the big bonuses of living a bit longer than most.)

Yesterday, today, it was possible to believe in spring. Things rushed out with such speed. That forgotten balminess was in the air. The birds were reassured. They sang, played, darted into nooks with feathers, bits of straw.

What happened to *anybody*, then? Eh?
It's the story of Roly's life, really; no more, no less?????? Does his great catastrophe put him in a different category? Most dogs don't have the pain.

Gazing on one tree, one apple.
One mushroom, one flower.
One flame.
Receiving and receiving — when, then, is Judgment Day? Never for us? But the Roar of Authority? That's just for the Take-off.
So, would I have anything useful to say to a person, directly? Perhaps not. Silent sympathy

seems the best of it. All the rest is in the words, on paper, to be heard or not.

I wasn't snuffling around these matters in the early days. Trudge, trudge, in and out the labyrinths of people's sensibilities and sorrows and mistakes. Better get in touch with Heaven, again. The strong lifting arm. The ruthless rush to the goal with the prize. Little drops — of blood?

Think of the opium poppy, wounded, scratched, oozing its white then black blood, scraped off in tiny harvests.

Amazement, wonder, breaks through, stops you in your tracks. Stays your hand?

Slowly, slowly proceed to the next thing. Cut down the wild prickly roses little by little. The pathos of the silver teapot.

If I could show — *explain*; what? The good, the glory, the splendour, the greatness, the beauty, the beneficence.

The essence. (A tinge of vanilla here, all these words are dusty, cobwebby, unworthy. A bird's song never has this outworn air, is never liable to misinterpretation — provokes no malice.)

Keep small. Keep the perfect drop in mind.

A weak woman spoke. Now the May strength returns and mighty feats are as bagatelle. Well, perhaps.

Half a year older, weaker, unfinished.
The Seasons.
The sensibilities.
Even in the garden.
Fuzzy-muzzy mind.
Try again, Milligan.
Begin again, Milligan.